THE LIFE OF
MAMMALS

THE LIFE OF
MAMMALS

David Attenborough

BBC

First published in 2002 by BBC Books,
an imprint of BBC Worldwide Ltd.,
80 Wood Lane, London W12 0TT

Frontispiece: a young orangutan, Sumatra

ISBN 0563 53423 0

Reproduction by Digitronix Ltd., Bradford
Printed in Great Britain by Butler and Tanner Ltd., Frome

CONTENTS

FOREWORD

We have a special regard for mammals. We are, after all, mammals ourselves. Indeed, we tend to talk as if mammals are the only kind of animals that exist – until, hard-pressed, we are forced to admit that birds, butterflies and bluebottles are also animals. Mammals, for the most part, have hair and are the only animals that rear their young on milk. Even so, there are a baffling number and variety of them. Over four and a half thousand. And they are more varied in shape and size than any other animal group. The biggest of them is the largest animal that has ever existed – the blue whale which is at least one and a half times as big as the biggest dinosaur. The smallest, the pygmy shrew, is so minuscule that it has to battle to subdue a beetle. Some mammals fly, some swim and some tunnel. Their diversity is so great that in order to sort them out in our minds we need to classify them into smaller groups. Faced with a mongoose in a zoo, we want to know what kind of mammal it is. Is it a kind of cat? Or maybe a dog? Or is it a giant rat?

The early naturalists classified mammals largely by diet. Lions and tigers, cats and dogs eat meat. So they were put together in a single group and called carnivores. Horses and zebras, antelope and deer eat plants. They, therefore, are herbivores. And rats, mice and squirrels that gnaw nuts and seeds are rodents.

There is good sense in categorising mammals in this simple and obvious way. An animal's body is, after all, shaped by the food it eats. Any weight-watcher or dedicated dieter knows that. But over many generations, eating the same kind of food can transform a species. So all the carnivores now have claws for catching their prey and sharp blade-like teeth with which to cut up their meals. Herbivores have molars at the back of their jaws that grind up plant tissues and special stomachs in which to process them. And rodents have two pairs of long curved teeth at the front of their mouths with which they chisel their way through nut shells.

Consequently this categorisation has stuck and the latest advances in molecular biology have shown that each of these groups is a true family in the sense that all its members are descended from the same ancestors. They also have not only common bodily characteristics but common habits. If an animal eats grass, it has to live where grass grows. That is in the open where there is plenty of light. Out there, a big animal has few places to hide. It must therefore find other ways to protect itself from predators. One method is to keep together. If you are surrounded by a crowd of others of your own kind, there is a good chance that an attacker will target one of them rather than you. So large grass-eaters tend to live in flocks or herds. That however, causes social problems. If you are male, then there will always be other males close by who will be trying to mate with the female you fancy. So you may have to fight. There is therefore a tendency for male grass-eaters to develop weapons and grow large and powerful. If you are a female, then you may have to submit to being rounded up with other females by large, aggressive males, or you may manage to exert your feminine choice and require, each season, to be courted with special rituals. So ultimately, the simple habit of eating grass leads not only to grinding teeth and complex stomachs, but elaborate horns and complicated social systems.

But mammals are, in evolutionary terms, extraordinarily enterprising and malleable. The ancient dynasties of herbivores and carnivores, and others of equal antiquity such as insectivores, produced some descendants that strayed from their original homes and while continuing to eat the same sort of food, looked for it in particularly demanding environments. Some of the carnivores went to sea to catch fish. Herbivores did the same in search of edible plants. Swimming also brought bodily changes over generations. So fish-eating seals came to resemble sea-grass-eating dugongs. The changes have been so wholesale that now, it is easier to understand the ways that their bodies work and their societies are organised, if such groups of different ancestry are considered together. So this book, and the television programmes that were being filmed at the same time as it was being written, have used diet as the basis on which to survey the entire group.

In describing this great range of species, I have used familiar names as far as possible. This, of course, risks imprecision for sometimes species may have several common names. Confusion can also come from exactly the opposite cause – a single common name can cover several different species. If, however, there is any doubt about the animal that is being described in the pages that follow, a reference to the index should resolve it for there, beside the alphabetically arranged common names, are the scientific names in italics.

Our relatedness to mammals makes it easy for us to empathise with them. We can imagine the feelings of a cow suckling her new-born calf, of a lion lazily lording it over his pride of lionesses, of a couple of chimpanzees grooming one another, even perhaps of a whale when it communicates with another across the vast distances of an ocean basin. Indeed, it is so easy that we are often tempted to think we understand other mammals better than, in fact, we do. The aim of this book is to amplify that instinctive understanding by examining the logics and processes that have moulded the bodies of mammals over the last hundred million years, and so enable us to comprehend the extraordinary efficiency and diversity of the mammals, the most complex and diverse of all animals on earth.

1

A WINNING DESIGN

Winter in the Arctic. The forests of fir and spruce are half buried in snow. Their sloping branches are burdened with it. It lies several feet deep all over the ground. The sun, when it comes, appears for only a few brief hours each day, hanging red and sullen just above the horizon before sinking down and disappearing for another eighteen hours or so. And as it vanishes, the bitter cold tightens its grip. There is no sound except for the distant muffled thud as a raft of snow slides off one of the slanting branches to explode in a cloud of white powder on the snowdrift beneath. Few places are more hostile to animal life. Amphibians would freeze solid here. Nor can reptiles tolerate such extreme and continuous cold. Further south, frogs and salamanders, lizards and snakes take shelter beneath the ground and relapse into torpor, their bodily processes suspended until the arrival of spring months later. But here the winter cold is so intense that they would die.

Yet there are animals here. A foot down beneath the surface of the snow a small entirely white creature the size of a pet hamster scurries along a tunnel. It is a collared lemming. It and other members of its family have excavated a complex home within this snow field. It has different kinds of accommodation. Some are sleeping chambers. Others are dining rooms where the sparse leaves of half-frozen grass still rooted in the earth are exposed and can be cropped. Some of the passage-ways that connect these chambers run along the ground beneath a roof of snow. Others tunnel their way through the snow itself and lead up to the outside world where one of the family may occasionally go to prospect for any vegetable food – a small seed perhaps – that might have recently arrived on the upper surface of the snow.

It costs the lemmings a great deal to survive here. They pay by using some of

11

their precious food to generate heat within their bodies so that their biochemical processes can continue to operate efficiently. Nonetheless, in order to keep their fuel costs to a minimum, they have to conserve as much heat as they can. And they do that by insulating their bodies with fur. It is dense and fine and covers them entirely except for their eyes.

Only one class of animals has hair – the mammals. A hair is composed of an inert substance called keratin. It grows constantly. Its root in the skin is wrapped around with nerve fibres so that its owner can sense any movement of the hair. Some mammals may appear to lack hair – hippos, whales and naked mole-rats, for example – but that loss is a secondary one, a specific adaptation to their particular environment. But even they, if their bodies are inspected closely, will be found to possess a few hairs, fringing their eyelids, in their ears, or other bodily crevices. Without hair, the majority of mammals would not be able to keep their bodies at proper operating temperature.

The ability to generate body heat internally is not limited to mammals. Birds, of course, can also do so. They insulate themselves extremely efficiently with feathers. Some, indeed, maintain their blood temperature at several degrees higher than any mammal. A few reptiles, which absorb their heat directly from the sun, are also able to do so to a limited extent. A female python, coiled protectively around her eggs and unwilling to leave them to go out and bask, can generate some of the warmth they need for development by spasmodic shivers of her muscles. Even fish can do so. Hunters such as shark and tuna, which rely on speed to capture their prey, keep their bodies significantly warmer than the surrounding water. Nonetheless, warm bodies are characteristic of all mammals and losing that warmth, for most, is lethal.

The group has another defining characteristic as well as hair. The name, Mammalia, comes from the Latin word meaning 'breast'. Breasts, however, are not diagnostic. Indeed many mammals do not possess them. It is milk, the product of the female's breast, that is so. The female lemming provides her young with it just as soon as they slip from her body in her snug nursery chamber within the snow. They are blind and seemingly helpless but within minutes of leaving her, they find the nipples on her underside and suck the warm nutritious liquid which contains all their young bodies need in order to grow at speed. It is milk that is the second mammalian hallmark.

When did the first animal equipped with those two important characters first appear? The question is not easily or directly answered for neither hair nor milk normally fossilises. Their presence in long extinct species has to be inferred from

their fossilised bones. Around two hundred and eighty million years ago a three-metre long reptile, Dimetrodon, appeared. It is a reasonable inference that it was warm-blooded because it had a tall skinny fin running along its backbone. When the animal basked in the sun, this fin could have served as a solar panel. Blood circulating through the capillaries it contained would have been warmed and could have carried that heat to the rest of its body. As a consequence Dimetrodon would have been able to summon energy immediately to catch other reptiles that were slower to warm. Pterosaurs, the flying contemporaries of the dinosaurs, are also thought to have been warm-blooded, for fossils have been found, both in Russia and in Germany that are surrounded by what appears to be the remains of hair. If they were indeed furry, then it seems clear that such an adaptation would have helped them retain the heat they needed to generate the energy for flapping their wings.

And around two hundred million years ago, small shrew-like creatures were scuttling through the litter of coarse fibrous leaves shed by ferns, cycads and conifers, the dominant vegetation of the time. They fed on invertebrates, chasing after ancestral millipedes and earwigs, perhaps even tackling small lizard-like

Polar bear suckling her cubs △

reptiles. Their fossils have been found in southern Africa and given the name Megazostrodon.

It may be that Megazostrodon's body was warmed initially simply as a by-product of its active life-style. Just as a car engine produces more heat the faster it runs, so the muscles of Megazostrodon's little body did so. That in itself enabled an animal to run faster, catch more prey, and produce more young. So over time, the ability became more ingrained. Eventually these small animals were able to maintain a little warmth in their bodies at all times and as a consequence, they were able to hunt at night, when other reptiles became inactive because of the drop in temperature.

This ability, however, did not bring Megazostrodon and its relations and descendants an immediate overwhelming advantage. They continued to scuttle around the feet of the dinosaurs for a further hundred million years and more until, for whatever reason, the dinosaurs and pterosaurs suddenly disappeared and a new age began. It was to belong to Megazostrodon, its relatives and descendants. The Age of Mammals had dawned.

And what could be the origins of milk, the second mammalian hall-mark? There at least we have two living animals that can provide us with clues. They are among the most extraordinary of all mammals, so extraordinary that they occupy a special subsection of the entire class, the monotremes. Both live today in Australia.

One of them is still, happily, quite a common animal. You can find it throughout Australia. Your first sight of it is likely to be a flat shield of coarse prickles, with about the same diameter as those of a porcupine but much shorter, lying flush with the surface of the ground. Touch it and the mat will give a convulsive heave and sink down a little further. The animal, whose back you have discovered, confident in the effectiveness of its armour of prickles, has no intention of exposing its more vulnerable underside. And that is likely to be all you will be able to see of it until darkness falls. Then the echidna will begin to stir. Suddenly it hoists itself up and starts to waddle away. It looks like a very large and exceedingly obese hedgehog with a small hairy face, beady eyes and a pointed snout. Its prickles, in fact, are somewhat sparse and set in a dense coat of short coarse hair. Its underside is covered with much longer hair and its toes are armed with powerful curved claws. With these it excavates the termites and ants which constitute the bulk of its food. It has no teeth but masticates its insects with rows of horny barbs on its tongue which grind against similar spines on the roof of its mouth.

An echidna rolling into a ball, Australia ▷
Echidna rolling on its back ▷

There are four subspecies of echidna in Australia, distinguished from one another by the length of their hair and the size of the long claw on the back legs which is used by the animal to scratch between its spines. There are yet another three species, sufficiently different from those in Australia to be given a different generic name, which live away to the north in the tropical island of New Guinea. They differ most obviously from their Australian relations, in that they have a cylindrical snout as long and as thin as a pencil. The mouth, at the end of this snout, is tiny, no wider than necessary to allow its thong-like tongue to emerge. They feed on earthworms and other invertebrates as well as ants and termites.

Echidnas are warm-blooded – just. Their body temperature is only about 32°C, which is about five degrees lower than ours. In the colder parts of their range, echidnas allow their body temperature to fall with coming of winter and become torpid. Elsewhere, where the cold is not so extreme, they manage to generate just sufficient heat to keep going. During the summer, the echidna's body need be no warmer than its surroundings.

So far, this description makes an echidna sound little more remarkable than a rather large and slightly chilly hedgehog. Its extraordinary nature does not become apparent until it reproduces.

There is virtually no external difference between male and female. Each has just one opening at the rear of its body through which both the sex ducts and the digestive tract empty. It is known as a cloaca, the Latin word for a drain. Reptiles and birds have a similar arrangement. It is for this reason that the echidna is known as a monotreme – a rather more refined way of saying 'one-holed' which is what that Greek-derived term means.

Reproduction starts with a strange courtship the details of which were unknown until quite recently. The female begins the process by producing a strong-smelling liquid. This attracts a male who begins to follow her. Another is likely to join it. Before long as many as a dozen may be trailing after her, nose to tail. This bizarre procession may stay with her, waddling through the bush for up to a month or so. Eventually the female brings things to a climax by starting to dig into the ground with her fore legs, leaving herself slightly up-ended. The males now start to dig as well and between them produce either a trench beside her or a circular rut surrounding her. Then one of them turns and starts to butt and shove the one behind it. Such scuffles break out all along the procession. One after another is pushed out of the trench until finally only one male remains. He now turns his attention to the female. He digs down a little way beside her.

Echidna baby suckling ▷

He reaches across and strokes her back with his front foot. She reacts by lowering her spines. Waves of ripples pass down her body. The moment of coupling has arrived. The male inserts his snout beneath her back end and lifts it slightly. A strange two-headed penis, each head with two openings, begins to protrude from his cloaca. He may now be facing either backwards or forwards, but either way he manages to insert his penis into her cloaca and the pair remain conjoined for up to four hours. Then they part and resume their solitary lives.

All this is extraordinary enough. But three or four weeks later, the most unexpected event of all takes place. The female lays an egg. It is the size of a small grape, with a soft leathery shell. The precise moment of emergence has not, so far, been witnessed by human beings. It may be that the female lies on her back, leaning slightly forwards. Somehow or other, however, the egg reaches a curved depression in her belly, like a shallow incomplete pouch, just a little in front of her cloaca. There it sticks to the hairs sufficiently firmly for it to stay in place as she moves about. Ten days after that, the parchment shell is slit by a small tooth on the tip of the nose of the infant within. Many reptiles and birds possess a similar tool – an egg-tooth. Eventually the hatchling manages to clamber free. It weighs only half a gram. Its eyes are covered by skin. Its

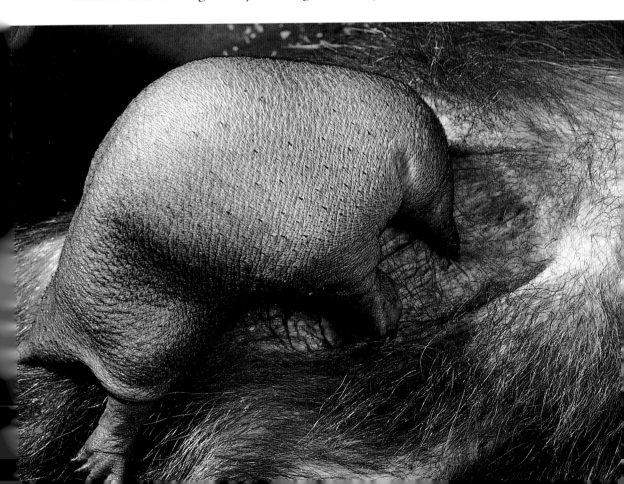

forelegs are sufficiently well formed to pull its weight and it clambers forward under its mother's belly, travelling six or seven times its own body length until it reaches the front end of her shallow pouch. Here, the hairs are different from those elsewhere on her body. About a hundred and fifty of them are rooted in enlarged follicles that exude a kind of white sweat. It is milk.

The infant creature sucks up milk though its tiny snout. It is so nutritious that the youngster grows rapidly. Within ten days, it increases its weight nearly thirty times. Spines begin to sprout on its back. Presumably this makes it a somewhat uncomfortable passenger. At any rate, after another ten days or so, the mother digs a burrow and deposits her youngster in it. She returns to feed it on milk for the next eight or nine months before finally her offspring is sufficiently well-grown for it to be able to start foraging by itself.

Only one other egg-laying animal in the world nourishes its hatchlings on milk. That too lives in Australia. It is the platypus, a furry short-legged creature about twenty inches long with a strange rubbery protrusion on the front of its head shaped like the beak of a duck. Just as the echidna has become specialised with a long sticky tongue and toothless jaws to feed on ants and termites, so the platypus has developed special equipment for finding food in water. It is an excellent swimmer, for although its toes end in strong claws, they are connected by a web of skin and when it splays its toes, its feet become very effective paddles. Its tail, though covered in fur, is flat like that of a beaver. This fur, which extends all over its body is so soft and fine that it prevents its body from chilling in the water. As a consequence it is able to maintain a much steadier body-temperature than an echidna can achieve and is able to swim in water within a degree of freezing.

Most remarkably of all, it is able to locate its prey with a sensory device that is unique among mammals. It has eyes – though they are very small and placed in a long muscular-walled groove. It also has ears, placed a little behind the eyes in the same groove. But when it dives, it draws the sides of the groove together so firmly that it becomes temporarily deaf and blind. Deprived of these two senses, it now finds its way around using its extraordinary rubbery beak. This is studded with pores which contain two kinds of sensory cells. Some can detect objects by touch. Others are sensitive to minute electrical charges such as those that are created by most living organisms.

Waving this bizarre remote-sensing device from side to side two or three times a second, it scans the river-bed as it swims above it. When it detects something promising – a freshwater shrimp, an insect larva or a small mollusc – it swiftly snaps up its discovery and tucks it into one of its cheek pouches. After

about a minute and a half below water, it surfaces. In a single night, it may collect as much as half its own body weight of food. Sometimes it floats on the surface, eating its catch. Otherwise, it retreats to its burrow in the river bank. There it empties its cheek pouches and masticates its meal, not with teeth for, like the echidna, it has none, but with grinding plates on its tongue and palate.

So one thing is clear. The platypus is a highly effective swimming mammalian hunter. But it also shares more characteristics with reptiles than any other mammal does. The bones of its shoulders resemble those of a therapsid, a small dinosaur, and its sperm is thread-like as is those of a reptile, rather than being club-shaped like all other mammals. But most obviously and dramatically of all, the platypus, like the echidna, lays eggs.

Courtship begins when the male starts to chase a female, who is normally slightly smaller. He grabs her tail. She grabs his. The two then slowly swim in circles. This may go on for several days until they copulate. By now the female has excavated a special burrow in the river bank. It is longer and deeper than the one she or her partner normally uses, and may extend for a hundred feet or so with several chambers leading from it. These she lines with grass and leaves, ferrying bundles of them across the water, tucked beneath her folded tail.

Platypus swimming, Australia △

No one yet has seen the actual act of laying but the female normally produces two eggs and incubates them by wrapping herself around them. After ten or eleven days, they hatch, the young cutting their way through the shell with an egg tooth as the hatching echidna does. Being a swimmer, she cannot carry her babies around with her in a pouch-like groove as the echidna does, but leaves them in her underground nest-chamber when she goes out to collect food for herself, plugging the mouth of the burrow with soil to keep them safe. When she returns she feeds them on milk oozing into a patch of her fur from scattered glands in the skin beneath.

Why these two remarkable animals – part-reptile, part-mammal – should have both survived in Australasia and nowhere else is still an unanswered question, but we do know that the platypus, at least, has been on that continent for a very long time. In 1985 a remarkably complete skull of an ancient platypus was found fossilised in rocks of north-western Queensland. The animal was not only somewhat larger than the platypus of today, its legs were proportionately longer and at the back of its jaw it had a few small teeth.

The site where this intriguing fossil was found, Riversleigh, is in sun-baked rocky bush country freckled with spinifex grass and gum trees. Twenty-five million years ago a group of shallow pools fed by a stream lay in depressions in the extremely ancient sandstone rocks. Occasionally, animals that came to drink at them from the surrounding bush fell in and were drowned. Others died nearby and their remains were washed down into the pools. As the millennia passed, the bones were covered with mud that accumulated in the bottom of the pools. Eventually as the continent of Australia drifted northwards and became drier, the pools themselves finally disappeared.

The rocks of Riversleigh now contain a detailed record of the animals that lived in this part of Australia from twenty-five million years ago until geologically recent times. They also show what else came to the pools in which those ancient platypus swam. The dinosaurs, by this stage, had gone but there were other reptiles of many kinds – skinks, geckos, huge python-like snakes and great numbers of frogs. There were giant flightless birds some standing nine feet high. But there were also other mammals, some of which we might immediately recognise as such. There was, for example, a small furry creature with a long bewhiskered snout, Ankotarinja, which looked very like a numbat.

The numbat is an insect-eater which runs around the Australian bush today, poking its snout into termite holes and ant-runs, flicking up insects with its long tongue. Ankotarinja's bones are so similar to a numbat's it seems a reasonable

Numbat, Australia ▷

inference that it behaved in the same sort of way. It also seems probable that it reproduced in a similar fashion. That, at the time, was revolutionary, for the numbat does not, like the platypus and the reptiles that were around during Ankotarinja's time, lay a shelled egg. It produces its young alive, at a very early stage in their development, unprotected by a shell.

The female appears to take little notice of the event. Several tiny pink worms emerge from her cloaca. They are very much smaller than a platypus egg. That is provisioned with a lot of yolk to nourish the developing embryo. These naked little worms, however, carry no food supply of any kind and unless they find one very quickly indeed they will die. They wriggle through their mother's fur to try and find the teats that are buried in it. But all do not succeed in doing so. She usually produces more tiny offspring than she has

teats. This race to milk is the first in a series of tests that a baby numbat has to win. It is a hurdle which ensures, right from the beginning, that only the strongest of her offspring will survive.

Drinking their mother's milk, the neonates grow very quickly indeed. By the time they are a week old, they are easily visible like small pink berries attached to her underside. They use her teats not only for their fuel supply, but as a way of holding on. Another week later and their fur is beginning to grow. After three months they are getting quite heavy for the mother to haul around and she dumps them in her nest, often within a hollow tree. She can now once again collect food for herself unencumbered but she returns every night to feed them with her milk. Six months after they first emerged, her babies are fully-grown and able to collect insects for themselves.

Carrying babies around during the early stages of their development no doubt brings advantages to both mother and her offspring. The young platypuses, encased within their shells, and abandoned whenever their mother needs to feed, are at the mercy of nest robbers; and their mother has to return regularly to the same place to incubate the eggs and, no doubt, to protect them from raiders if she can. Even so, baby numbats, clinging to their mother's underside, look alarmingly vulnerable. Other Australian mammals, however, have evolved additional safety measures.

The koala is one. About 35 days after a pair have mated, a small embryonic baby, glistening pink, blind, with well-formed front legs but hind limbs that are little more than buds, emerges from its mother's cloaca. It is only 19 millimetres – three quarters of an inch – long. It hauls and wriggles its way along its mother's underbelly. She may lick her bristly fur to create a slightly moistened path ahead of it, but if she does, that is the only help she gives it. Within a few inches, and fewer minutes, it finds a fold in the skin of her belly. The neonate wriggles into it and finds itself in a warm moist pouch. There in the darkness, it somehow discovers a teat. It fastens its tiny mouth around it and takes its first sip of milk. The technical name given to this admirable nursery is marsupium, which in Latin means 'purse' and all Australian mammals that produce their unshelled young at a very early stage in their development are known as marsupials, even if some of them, like the numbat, do not actually possess one.

And there are many of them. They have spread over all Australia to exploit all its many environments.

The koala itself is a highly specialised climber with short muscular legs and feet capable of a very firm grasp. It also has a highly specialised digestive system

Koala with young, Australia ▷

that enables it to feed almost entirely on gum leaves which are so full of toxins that few other animals can eat them.

Dunnarts are marsupials the size of mice. Their teeth, however, unlike those of mice, are not chisel-shaped for gnawing but sharp as needles. They use them to collect tiny invertebrates, insects, spiders and even occasionally small lizards. Their newly emerged young are barely the size of grains of rice.

Quolls, as big as cats, are also well-equipped with long dagger-like teeth on either side of their jaws with which they kill bigger prey. They, like numbats, are marsupials without a marsupium. A female produces as many as thirty neonates, but only has eight teats, so nearly three quarters of them die within minutes of their birth.

There is a marsupial mole which looks somewhat like its European equivalent. It has lost its eyes and has on the front of its head a large horny shield with which it pushes its way through the soil. Its pouch, not surprisingly, faces backwards. Were it to point in the other direction, it would fill with earth.

The honey possum is a nectar feeder and has developed a long tongue with which to flick up the sweet liquid from the depths of flowers.

△ *Dunnart with prey, Australia*

Eastern quoll with young ▷
Marsupial mole with its prey, Australia ▷

The wombat, about the size of a European badger, is a digger which excavates substantial holes for itself as homes but, unlike the badger, lives primarily on grasses.

Until very recently, there was also a marsupial equivalent of a wolf. The thylacine was not quite as big as a wolf and it had broad black stripes across the rear half of its body. It flourished in the woodlands of the south, particularly in those that cover most of the island of Tasmania which separated from the continent some twelve thousand years ago. About four thousand years ago, Asian peoples, visiting Australia perhaps to trade with the Aboriginal inhabitants (who had been there for forty thousand years), brought with them a dog we now call the dingo. They did not stay – but the dingoes did. They spread through the continent hunting very much the same sort of prey that the thylacine depended upon. As the dingoes increased, so the numbers of thylacine dwindled. But the dingo never crossed the Bass Strait into Tasmania and there thylacines continued to flourish.

Then, two centuries or so ago, human settlers from Europe introduced sheep. The thylacine preyed on the lambs and in return was hunted by the human settlers. As a result of this persecution by farmers, the competition from dingoes, and the fact that most of the woodlands where it lived were felled to provide pasture for sheep, the thylacine disappeared all over continental Australia. In Tasmania it held its own for much longer, but by the 1920's it had largely gone from there as well. The last wild specimen was caught in 1930 and died in 1936. There are those who believe that the marsupial wolf still haunts the forests of Tasmania or even – though this must be still less probable – the bush of Queensland. But the likelihood is that it is now extinct and the only picture we shall ever get of it as a living breathing animal comes from a jerky black and white film of a captive specimen, pacing its cage in the London Zoo and yawning prodigiously to display its formidable teeth.

The most famous marsupials of all, of course, are the grazers that live on the wide Australian plains, the kangaroos. The red kangaroo is the largest of all surviving marsupials. The male stands over five feet tall. The image of a female kangaroo with her baby, a joey, peering amiably from the pouch on her belly is the very symbol and epitome of Australia's unique wildlife. But why should kangaroos hop?

It may be that sitting back on your haunches is a more convenient way of moving at speed if you are encumbered with a heavy burden in a satchel slung in front of you. Such a posture also frees the hands so that you can collect bits

◁ *Young common wombat, Mt. Kosciuszko, Australia*

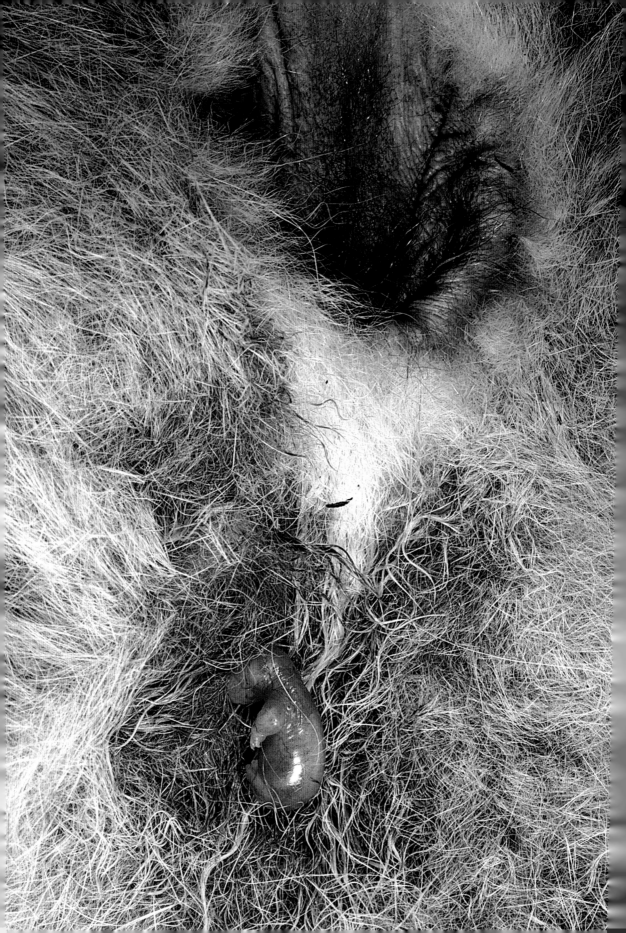

of food that are more easily picked up with paws than lips. The little rat kanga-roo, which is indeed the size of a rat, illustrates how the process may have started. Rambling through the undergrowth, it moves on all fours, but its front legs are shorter than its hind and it uses them to pick up insects and seeds. And then, if it needs to move at speed, it bounds away on its hind legs. Two-legged leaps are, in fact, a very efficient way of moving and require less energy than is needed by a four-legged runner moving at a similar speed.

Hopping is so successful a way of getting around that kangaroo-shaped mar-supials now come in many different sizes and occupy a surprisingly wide variety of habitats. Some – the pademelons – live in open woodland. They have bodies about two feet long, excluding their tail. Rock wallabies – miniature kangaroos scarcely bigger than terrier dogs – live on cliffs and when startled bounce away from one ledge to another and sometimes manage to travel straight up what ap-pear to be sheer rock faces. They have rubbery granulated soles to their feet which give them a tyre-like grip.

But the place where kangaroos are seen at their noblest is grazing out on the open plains. Eating grass wears down teeth very quickly. Grazers elsewhere, such as rabbits, deal with this problem by having open roots to their teeth so that they can continue to grow, replacing the steady loss at their upper end. Kangaroos deal with wear in a different way. New molars grow at the back of their jaw and steadily move towards the front, replacing worn ones which sim-ply drop out. However, the animal cannot continue doing this indefinitely. Af-ter the fourth pair has been ground down, there are no more replacements and the kangaroo will then starve to death even if, in its aged condition, it manages to escape other hazards.

Just as grazers elsewhere, such as antelope and deer, live in herds, so kanga-roos live in mobs. A group of a dozen or so is very common and sometimes there are many more living and feeding together. In such circumstances, there is competition between rival males for the females, and fights break out. Ante-lope fight with their horns, deer with their antlers. Kangaroos do so with those powerful hind legs. After preliminary boxing with their short fore-legs they will lean back on their muscular tails, like marksmen on shooting sticks, and strike out with their back legs. The muscles that power bounding leaps up to 8 yards long now deliver blows with such force that their claws can rip open an opponent's belly.

It is the kangaroos that have brought the marsupial method of reproduction

◁ *Kangaroo neonate crawling up to its mother's pouch*

to its most efficient level. A young female kangaroo produces her first neonate about 36 days after mating. It makes its astonishing journey into her pouch and starts to suckle. Almost immediately afterwards, she becomes fertile again and one of the males in her group, detecting from her smell that this is the case, will be quick to mount her. The egg within her that has been fertilised does not, however, develop immediately. Instead it lies dormant in her womb. Her pouch is already occupied. When that baby has been there for about 300 days, it is sufficiently well-formed to pay visits to the outside world and to find other food to supplement its milk. This decrease in suckling has a profound effect on its mother. The egg in her womb begins to develop.

Now she has two youngsters – one still spending much of its time in her pouch, one developing in her womb. Another 33 days pass and her second offspring emerges from her cloaca, clambers into her pouch and finds a teat of its own. Her first-born, now spending much of its time outside the pouch, hopping about beside her, is growing fast. It returns regularly for milk, some-times not even bothering to clamber into her pouch but merely poking its

◁ *Mother kangaroo with joey in her pouch*   *Grey kangaroos fighting* △

head inside to reach the nipple. The milk from this nipple has now changed. It is richer in fat which is what the youngster needs at this stage. So now she is producing two kinds of milk — one for her offspring who has not quite left home and calls in from time to time, and one for the new long-term lodger which contains more carbohydrates.

Two weeks after her older offspring left her pouch for the first time, she came into season again and once more she had mated. Now she is at her most productive. One of her young still requires her milk but spends hours of the day outside her pouch and is on the verge of independence. A second is within her pouch but still not properly formed; and a third is in her womb waiting to develop just as soon as her second ventures out of her pouch for the first time.

This way of producing young is at least as efficient as that of similar-sized animals with similar life-styles elsewhere in the world. Sheep, after all, normally only produce one or two lambs a year. The marsupial method is particularly suited to conditions in Australia where droughts are not uncommon. At such times, a female kangaroo's milk supply will dry. The youngster that is on the verge of independence will now have to leave her early to fend for itself, and the younger one in the pouch will be aborted. She herself will make the minimum demand on the meagre pasture around her and she has a fertile dormant egg within her womb ready to start its development just as soon as conditions improve.

The variety of marsupials was once even greater than it is today. Only fifty thousand years ago there were some giants — a huge kangaroo that stood over nine feet tall which browsed the trees; a marsupial equivalent of a lion with fangs of a comparable size; and the biggest of all known marsupials, Diprotodon, that was the size and approximate shape of a bear. We have no direct evidence, of course, as to how these extinct creatures reproduced, since genitalia and pouches of skin do not fossilise, but fortunately there are many other features typical of marsupials which do. In particular, there are characters in the teeth that are shared by all Australian marsupials, both living and fossil, that allow us to be certain that animals with them in their jaws can properly be classified as marsupials. It comes as a surprise, however, to discover that the earliest of these fossil forms was discovered not in Australia at all but in the chalk rocks of South America. How could that have happened?

Australia was once part of a great super-continent. Forty-five million years ago, infinitely slow forces operating deep below the earth's crust caused this land mass to separate into three fragments. Each had a very different fate. Australia

remained an island, never again having direct contact with any other land except for the island of New Guinea to the north. So Australia's marsupials evolved in isolation and produced the great range of types that has been described. A second fragment drifted down towards the South Pole. As it travelled, it became progressively colder until finally all its animals and plants were exterminated and the land became cloaked in a vast accumulation of ice, in places miles thick. This is Antarctica. Direct evidence that it was once inhabited by marsupials can now only come from its rocks. Since most of them are still covered by ice, such evidence is very difficult to obtain, but the fossilised bones of a rat-sized snouted marsupial have at last been found in them. The third fragment, South America, moved in the opposite direction and eventually collided with North America. That continent had its own population of mammals that had evolved in the northern hemisphere. Some of these creatures took advantage of the newly created land bridge and spread across it to mingle and compete with South America's marsupials.

Virginia opossum, North America △

They were so successful that many of South American native marsupials disappeared, including some large carnivorous species. Nonetheless over eighty different marsupials still survive today in South America's forests. They are nowhere near as varied as their distant Australian cousins. Collectively they are known as opossums. They range in size from a mouse to a cat. All have long, much bewhiskered snouts and most have prehensile tails. Some spend most of their time on the ground. Others prefer life in trees. In diet they are omnivores. Animals and vegetables, insects and reptiles, fruit and nectar, they seem only too happy to sample them all. Only one has a specialised life style. This is the yapok or water opossum. Its body, not counting its tail, is over a foot long and it has three broad whitish stripes across its grey furry back. Its hind feet are webbed and it is a powerful swimmer feeding on small fish, crayfish and other water creatures.

The underwater life might not seem an attractive proposition for an animal that carried its young in a pouch for several months. No Australian marsupial has adopted it. The yapok's pouch, however opens backwards. The edges of its opening are covered with long hairs and are rich in glands that produce an oily secretion. A powerful sphincter muscle enables a female to pull her pouch shut so firmly that no water seeps in as she swims. The young within are not therefore in danger of drowning. On the other hand, it might seem that they could well suffocate, trapped inside this water-tight bag as their mother paddles about and dives in search of food, but they are able to tolerate very low oxygen levels for many minutes at a time. Remarkably, the male has a pouch as well. He also has a scrotum covered in mustard-coloured fur. It is said that when he swims he draws his scrotum into his marsupium, though exactly what muscles he uses to achieve this trick, which must presumably help with his streamlining, is not immediately obvious.

One of these opossums is so successful that it has managed to travel along the land bridge of Panama and into North America. The Virginia opossum, whose ancestors came from South America, is now found widely through the eastern half of the United States. When you encounter one in the woods, you know immediately that it is something odd. It is about the size of a cat, with rather shorter legs and it is likely to be clambering along a branch. Its hairy coat is long and coarse. When it snarls at you – which it probably will, for they are bold animals – it hisses alarmingly and displays an extraordinarily large number of teeth. You won't have time to count them but there are fifty. And alone of all the mammals of North America, it has a long naked tail which it curls around a

◁ *Virginia opossum displaying its prehensile tail, Florida* branch gripping it so tightly that it serves as an extra limb. If you have found the animal in spring and it is a female, you may be lucky enough to see the opossum's most unexpected characteristic of all. She may have as many as a dozen mouse-sized babies that have clambered out of her pouch and are clinging to her back.

And Virginia opossums have one further surprise. If you corner one, it may suddenly collapse and lie motionless on the ground. You can touch it – if you are bold enough – and it will show no signs of life. Its heart-beat will be barely de-tectable. You may fear that, for some reason, you have brought about its death, for it will lie like this for hours. But it is, as they say in Virginia, 'playing possum', for after some time, it will suddenly get to its feet and run swiftly away. Perhaps this behaviour developed as a defensive strategy but against what kind of attacker isn't clear since if it was being hunted for its flesh, its attacker would hardly be deterred from ripping it apart by the fact that it was apparently dead.

There is no doubt that the Virginia opossum is an extremely successful animal. It is not very long-lived – two years is its normal life span in the wild – but since in that time it may produce over twenty young, it has little difficulty in maintain-ing its numbers. Indeed, during the last hundred years or so, it has expanded its territory, moving not only north as far as the Canadian border but westwards into the state of Colorado. Human settlers, for some reason, introduced the spe-cies into California and these remarkable animals have done well there too. Nonetheless, when faced with direct competition from mammals that originated in the north, many other kinds of marsupials have disappeared. Why should this be?

The obvious and fundamental way in which northern mammals differ from marsupials is in the manner by which they nourish their young during the first stages of their lives. Instead being expelled down their mother's birth canal and crawling like vulnerable little worms across her belly and into a pouch, the young northern mammal remains inside its mother's body in her womb. There it is fed by way of a remarkable and complex device, her placenta. This is a pad attached to the side of the womb and linked to the developing baby by a pipe, the umbili-cal cord. Blood passes from the wall of the mother's womb into the placenta. There it exchanges oxygen and carbon dioxide, nutrients and waste materials with blood in the arteries of the developing baby. Only when her baby is at a much more developed stage than any newly emerged marsupial, is it expelled into the outside world. In some species – bears and human beings for example – these newly-born young are still far from fully developed. In others – among them antelopes and elephants – they are able to walk independently within minutes. But all, for some time to come, will still depend for succour on their mothers' milk. From her mammae. Like marsupials, they are, after all, mammals.

All mammals are descended from some distant reptilian ancestor. They separated at a very early date into marsupials and placentals. It is not the case that marsupials represent an intermediate stage in the evolution of placental mammals. The two anatomies are different, independent solutions to the problem of rearing young. Both worked so well that they led to a great range of specialised forms, each adapted to a particular way of collecting food and most with a parallel in the other continent that is superficially similar. But whereas those in Australia became isolated on their continent, those in the north spread over all Asia, Europe and Africa. Ultimately, they travelled down into South America, and even into the air and the sea. It is those that will occupy the rest of this book.

2

THE INSECT HUNTERS

The northern hemisphere, sixty five million years ago, had its own super continent. Like that in the south of which Australia was a part, it too would eventually split in pieces and these fragments would become Europe, Asia and North America. At the time that this break-up occurred, the dinosaurs still flourished and the earth's vegetation differed considerably from that of today. The flowering plants were in the first stages of their evolution. Water lilies studded the surface of the lakes and magnolia trees flowered in the woodlands. The forests, however, were still rich in coniferous trees, cycads and tree ferns. There were – and had been for some two hundred million years – a host of small invertebrates inhabiting the land. Worms were tunnelling in the soil. Centipedes, millipedes and other multi-legged creatures were creeping through the leaf-litter. There were hordes of ants and termites, though neither had yet started to congregate in great colonies. Swarms of insects were flying through the air and spiders were constructing their silken traps to catch them. These tiny creatures were largely if not entirely ignored by the dinosaurs. But scuttling around among the dinosaurs were small furry warm-blooded back-boned animals the size of rats. For them, the varied invertebrates were a rich source of food. Some have continued to feast on them from that day to this.

As a group, these creatures are known as insectivores, though many of them eat a great variety of other small invertebrates as well as insects. Typical of the earliest of them are today's shrews. These, like their ancestors, are very small. Indeed the pygmy shrew that lives in parts of southern Europe is the smallest of all mammals alive today. Its body, not counting its tail is scarcely more than two inches long and it weighs less than two grams. It is so small that it can chase a beetle down a worm-hole. And it does.

There are over three hundred different species of shrew and they inhabit

every continent except Australia and the Antarctic. The pygmy is exceptionally tiny, the midget of its family, but none are much bigger than a house mouse. Being small for a mammal brings one particular problem. Small bodies lose heat very much faster than large ones. That is because the ratio between surface area and volume is greater in small objects than in big ones. Shrews keep their bodies as far as possible at 37°C, which is the usual operating temperature for most mammals. They insulate themselves, as most mammals do, with coats of fur, but even the finest, densest, longest fur cannot adequately insulate the minuscule shrews. To compensate, they have to stoke their boilers continuously. That is to say, they eat prodigiously. Every day, they consume three times their own body weight.

Warm bodies might be expensive to maintain but they brought those first shrews one great advantage. Their owners were able to search for prey when other hunters such as small reptiles were cold and unable to summon up the necessary energy. Darkness would not have troubled them any more than it does their descendants today. If you spend most of your time half-buried, rummaging through the leaf litter, sight is of little value and the eyes of shrews are tiny. In some species they are buried deep in the fur. The animals find their

Pygmy shrew with earthworm, England △

way around by touch, using the long whiskers which sprout abundantly on their very pointed snouts. They also use sound, making squeaks, many parts of which are so high-pitched that they are beyond the range of our ears. These calls almost certainly serve as a simple kind of echo-location. Even we, if we walk into an unknown room in pitch darkness, can get some idea of its size from the sound of our footsteps. The shrews' squeaks help them in a way that is fundamentally the same but much more complex and informative. Their system however, is simplicity itself compared with the heights of sophistication that some of their descendants were to bring to echo-location within the next few million years.

Everything in the life of shrews is done at astonishing speed. Their hearts, almost unbelievably, beat twelve hundred times a minute. They take seventy breaths in the same time. When one tackles an earthworm, which may be several times longer than itself, it does so with manic vigour and ferocity. As it wrestles with a worm, it stabs it with its lower incisor teeth. Some species also inject their prey with venom of such toxicity that it will kill a small animal. It can even cause a human being intense and long-lasting pain though their teeth are so small that they are unlikely to puncture a human being's skin.

△ *The long whiskers of a pygmy shrew, France*

Shrews act with equal vigour when they meet one another. They are normally solitary animals, each maintaining its own hunting territory. If a resident encounters an intruder, both will freeze momentarily, their bodies outstretched and stiff, their snouts thrust forward as they establish one another's identity. Then they shriek angrily at one another with short staccato cries. One stamps its front feet and they join battle. They rise on their hind legs and lash out with their front legs. They grapple with one another and bite at each other's head. Eventually, one gives up and rushes off. The winner then marks his victory with a drop of smelly urine which proclaims the fact that this territory is his.

Mating is conducted in the same frenetic fashion. There is virtually no courtship. Initial grapplings are ferocious, the female sometimes biting the male so severely that she draws blood. Such fights presumably enable a female to satisfy herself that the male she is wrestling with is strong enough to be a suitable mate. If she decides that he is acceptable, she signals the fact by turning her rump towards him and wagging her tail. His aggressive barks change to a softer, high-pitched call. The two then copulate.

A female shrew makes a very well-built nest of dried leaves. Like marsupials, her genital and digestive tracts empty into a common canal, a cloaca. Her babies, when they leave her body from this pore, are much better developed than any marsupial young on its way to a pouch since they have been nurtured in a womb. Nonetheless, they are minute. They are born in litters of about half a dozen, and are at even greater hazard from losing heat than their mother, for they weigh only about a gram and they are born naked. But their mother's mammalian inheritance – her nipples and her milk – enables them to grow very rapidly and within three weeks they are clad in fur and sufficiently well-grown to venture outside the nest. Soon after their birth, their mother vacates the nest and looks for a new one. The young of several species take special measures to ensure that they do not get lost at this early stage in their lives. As their mother emerges from the nest, one of her babies bites her rump and holds on with its teeth. The others cling on behind in a similar way so that as she rushes off to find a new home, she and her offspring all keeping in step with one another, seem to be one large organism like a furry snake sliding through the grass at speed.

Insects and other terrestrial invertebrates occur virtually everywhere and insectivores pursue them wherever they are found. To do so, they have developed a wide range of adaptations. Several members of the shrew family have taken to the water to collect aquatic insects including water beetles and the larvae of flies, as well as other small invertebrates such as worms, leeches, and snails. They will even tackle newts and little fish. Heat loss could be even swifter in water than on land, but the water shrew's fur is so fine that it traps air and the animal, when it dives, looks like an animated silver bubble. The European water shrew has developed webbed feet fringed with long hairs which help it to propel itself under water. The little animal weighs so little and its feet spread its weight so widely that it can even skitter for several yards across the surface of the water.

Other insectivores, the desmans, also look for their meals in water. They are sufficiently different from shrews to be placed in a different family but they are nonetheless quite closely related. There are only two species of desman, one in northern Spain and Portugal, and one in Russia. They too have webbed feet – half so on the front feet, fully on the hind – but they have other aquatic adaptations as well. Their tails are broad, fringed with stiff hairs and serve as a combined propeller and rudder. Their ears have valves that can be closed at will. Most impressive of all, their snouts are elongated into a kind of snorkel, so that the animal can breathe air even though its body is completely submerged.

They swim – but they also burrow. The Russian desman makes a hole with

an entrance that is below water level so that it can come and go from its nest without being seen by land-living animals. One relative of the desmans is also a swimmer but spends most of its time digging. This is the star-nosed mole of North America. It is the owner of the oddest-looking of all mammalian sense organs – a small pink fleshy star resembling a flower that is attached to the very tip of its nose. The lobes of this star are richly supplied with blood vessels and nerves and have such a sensitive touch that the animal, foraging along the bottom of a lake or burrowing in the earth of the bank, can use it to locate and establish the edibility of five separate small invertebrates in the space of a single second.

Cousins of the star-nose – the true moles – may also be descended from swimming ancestors like desmans, for all of them are still very competent in the water when needs be. Nonetheless they spend virtually their entire lives tunnelling though the ground. Like the star-nosed mole, they have immensely strong shoulders, stocky fore-legs, and hands that have been turned into spades almost as broad as they are long. Their fur is very fine and short and does not lie

Star-nosed mole surfacing, North America △

in any particular direction so that it does not brush awkwardly whether the animal is moving forwards or backwards along its tunnels.

Living permanently below ground solves several problems. The animal is out of the sight and reach of most predators; and it does not have to deal with great variations of temperature. Nonetheless, a mole's life is full of labour. To establish an underground territory for itself, it may dig five hundred yards of tunnels, pushing the excavated soil up vertical shafts and out on to the surface to create the familiar mole hills that so infuriate proud lawn-owners and tenders of golfing greens.

Each mole, male or female, maintains its own tunnel system and seldom trespasses into another's – except at breeding time. It makes regular three or four hour patrols of these tunnels, collecting up any invertebrates that may have dropped into them, or digging swiftly to secure those it might detect lying in the soil close to the walls. Earthworms are particular favourites. When it eats one, it pulls it through its fore-paws so that not only is any mud cleared from the worm's skin but the earth in its gut is squeezed out, like toothpaste from a tube. If the hunting has been good, however, a mole may not consume its worm immediately. Instead it will paralyse it with a bite and then deposit it in a store where it will survive until such time as the mole needs to eat it. Larders containing over a thousand such paralysed worms have been discovered.

Insects, at the time that the first mammalian insect-eaters appeared, not only swarmed on the ground, they also flew. No doubt, some of the small insectivores, clambering up tree trunks and running along branches looking for their food, started to try and catch them. Perhaps they began by leaping and then, as they became better adapted physically to doing so, their leaps extended into glides. Whatever the intermediate stages, we know for certain that by fifty million years ago, some had succeeded in catching flying insects, for the remains of an early mammal was found in rocks of that age that once were mud on the bottom of a lake in Wyoming. It was superbly preserved. In the place within its delicate skeleton where its stomach had been there was a little cluster of insect remains. And it was dramatically clear what method the little mammal had used to collect them. Its fingers were hugely elongated and supported a skinny membrane the impression of which was still visible. It was a bat.

Revolutionary though this development was, the bodily modifications necessary to achieve it were comparatively simple. It was largely a matter of a change in physical proportions. Shorten the upper-arm; leave the thumb free but greatly

extend the rest of the fingers; extend the skin from the side of the neck across the fingers and down to the leg – and you have a bat's wing.

Today there are two very different kinds of bat – small insect-eating ones, and larger ones that live largely if not entirely on fruit. Whether both kinds evolved at the same time is a matter of some debate, but it is quite certain that the insect-eaters are related to shrews. Nearly seven hundred different species have been identified and there could be still more as yet undiscovered. The biggest of them is the size of a small rat. The smallest, the hog-nosed bat of Thailand, sometimes called the bumble-bee bat, rivals the pygmy shrew as the smallest of all mammals. Its body, discounting its wings, is around the same size – around two inches long and weighing about two grams. It is a reasonable guess that the shrew-like ancestors of these bats used high-pitched sounds to find their way in the dark, just as living shrews do today. It is no surprise therefore that their descendants still do the same. What is surprising – indeed astonishing – is the way in which bats have elaborated those simple ultrasonic squeaks into the superb navigational and hunting system that they use today.

They generate these sounds with the larynx in their throat and emit them

Long-eared bat in flight △

through both the nose and the mouth. Many bats focus the sound beam using a structure called a nose-leaf that surrounds the nostrils. This varies widely in shape from species to species. There are bowls, slits, leaves, vertical spears, horse-shoe-shaped cups and shapes that are so complex and convoluted that they cannot be compared with any simple object. Many are mobile so that their owners can vary the width and character of the beam they project. The sounds themselves are emitted as a series of extremely short stabs. They are so high-pitched that they are far beyond the range of our own ears. But they are extremely powerful. If we were able to transpose them down at their true volume they would sound as loud to us as a jet engine.

The intensity and frequency of these sonar probes varies according to the bat's needs. Those used for general navigation are not as intense as those which the bat makes when homing in on a particular target. All such sounds are reflected back from surrounding objects and received by the bats' large ears which also vary in shape from species to species. These echoes, are, of course very faint, so a bat's sense of hearing has to be extremely sensitive. If the bat heard its shrieks with its own hyper-sensitive ears, it would deafen itself, but it is able to switch off its sense of hearing every time it emits a stab of sound. And it has to do that as frequently as two hundred times a second.

As the bat flies, it scans the sky in front of it, swinging its head rapidly from side to side and adjusting the contours of the transmitting apparatus on its nose. From the timing of echoes it receives with its huge mobile ears, it is able to tell how far away an object is and whether it is static or mobile; and from the quality of those echoes it can deduce the nature of the surface that reflected them and therefore the likely identity of the object concerned. And all this is done as the bat flutters through the air at up to 40 miles an hour.

Although insects are the main-stay of these bats, some tackle bigger prey. One particularly large one has learned how to pluck small frogs that sit at night – rashly – calling on logs. Another species trails its feet, armed with hooked claws, in the surface of water and gaffs small fish. The vampire, notoriously, drinks the blood of other mammals such as horses and even human beings. To do that, it may land directly on its victim, but more usually, it settles on the ground beside it and supporting itself on its elbows, creeps stealthily towards its target. It delicately shaves the hair and topmost layer of a small patch of skin on its victim using its front incisor teeth which are triangular with razor sharp edges. Its canine teeth are equally sharp but flattened laterally and with these it cuts two grooves in the wound. At the same time, it produces copious spittle which contains both a mild

anaesthetic and an anticoagulant so that its victim is unaware of the attack and blood continues to ooze from the wound. The vampire, crouched alongside, then laps up the blood with its tongue.

The bats' distant insectivore ancestors were creatures of the night and the bats themselves have remained so. Birds had already claimed the skies before the bats evolved, so ever since bats first appeared there have been only too many sharp-eyed swift-flying predators around during the day for them to risk flying about at that time. Bats therefore have to find good secure homes in which to hide during the daylight hours. Caves are ideal. Conditions within them are usually very stable – cool in summer and relatively warm in winter – and bats are quick to colonise them. Some particularly large caverns may provide a home to several million bats. But bats have also become very ingenious in creating homes for themselves.

Some rely on camouflage. In the swamps of Florida, many of the trees are hung with air plants, commonly called Spanish moss. The hoary bat has grey

Vampire bat feeding on a cow, Trinidad △

fur and hangs itself in the middle of a dangling clump where it is virtually invisible. In Africa, woolly bats suspend themselves from the threads of the webs of colonial spiders. In the forests of South-east Asia, a tiny bat with an extremely flattened head seeks out a bamboo stem with a slit in its side. The slit was made when a beetle grub that hatched within the bamboo stem finally changed to an adult and gnawed its way free. Such a slit is just wide enough for this bat to squeeze through, and common enough for such bats to sleep nowhere else but within bamboos. In South America, there are plants, Heliconia, whose new leaves emerge from their buds tightly furled. As they slowly unroll their underside provides an inviting shelter. But as a home, it has two disadvantages. First, the leaf does not stay that way for long, which means that a lodger has to continually move to new quarters. Second, the surface of the young leaf is as smooth as glass. But the sucker-footed bat has developed suction pads on the soles of its feet that enable it to get a grip – though to make sure that the suction is perfect it licks its soles before it attaches itself.

Perhaps the most unexpected home of all is that used by a New Zealand bat, the short-tailed. It lives in burrows – not ones that it takes over second-hand from some other creature, but burrows that it digs for itself. It is an evolutionary development that parallels that made by birds in a most remarkable way.

New Zealand split away from Australia even before the first marsupials appeared there. At that time, New Zealand's only back-boned animals were a few species of reptile – though no snakes or large lizards – and some early birds. In due course, other birds managed to fly across the ocean to the islands. The land they found suited them very well indeed. The floors of the forests were full of edible insects and plants yet there were no mammalian predators there to harry birds as was the case in Australia and other continents. Why waste energy on flying if there are no dangers in going down to the ground and plenty to eat there? Many of New Zealand's birds therefore abandoned flight and today the islands have a flightless parrot, rail and moorhen. The short-tailed bat that eventually found its way across the Tasman Sea and reached New Zealand reacted in a similar sort of way.

While the short-tail has certainly not lost the power of flight, it readily alights on the ground and runs around in a very agile way. Wings with a span several times the length of the body might be thought a considerable impediment on the ground, but the short-tail has evolved a very neat way of tucking them away. It walks on the back of its wrists so that the greatly elongated fingers that support the wing membranes point upwards and slot neatly in grooves

◁ *Tent-making bats roosting beneath a heliconia leaf, South America*

on the arm. The membrane which in flight stretches from thigh to thigh and encloses the tail, is rolled up and furled away beneath a narrow band of skin, so that its tail, already short, becomes invisible.

Its hind legs, which in so many other bats are little more than suspension hooks, are stout and muscular and help it tunnel its way into the leaf litter. It pushes aside the leaf fragments with its tiny snout. Every now and then its head appears above the surface and then it ducks back again and continues its hunt for food. Often groups of a dozen or so will hunt close together, so that invertebrates fleeing from one move straight into the path of another. The short-tail is thus able to make much more substantial meals than its cousins who have to live on little more than mosquitoes. It will take fragments of fruit and seeds, beetle larvae and even do battle with New Zealand's giant flightless crickets, the weta, which may weigh at least twice as much as the bat itself.

When did the short-tailed bat embark on this return evolutionary journey? There are no fossils to tell us, but there is, nonetheless, evidence – from a flower. New Zealand has only one fully parasitic plant, Dactylanthus. It is a parasite which fastens itself to the root of a tree and draws all its sustenance from the tree's sap. It thus has no need for either leaves or stem and exists only as a fleshy rhizome, until the time comes to flower. Then a bud pushes its way up through the

50

△ *New Zealand short-tailed bat attacking a*
cricket   *Common tenrec, Madagascar* ▷

soil and opens on the forest floor. The Maori name for it is *pua o te reinga* which means roughly, 'flower from the spirit world'. This flower, sitting on the ground, has brown woody petals, a musky smell and produces liberal quantities of nectar. Those are the characteristics of flowers that are pollinated by small ground-living mammals. But there are no such mammals in New Zealand and Dactylanthus occurs nowhere else in the world. Careful surveillance by scientists with night-vision cameras eventually showed that the pollinator is in fact the short-tailed bat. Such close partnerships between plants and pollinators take a long time to evolve. The short-tailed bat must have returned to the way of life of its far distant shrew-like ancestors tens of thousands of years ago.

One other group of insectivores can rival the shrews in its similarity to the very earliest of northern hemisphere mammals. These are the tenrecs and their close cousins, the otter-shrews. Like true shrews, they are nocturnal, find their way around with the help of abundant sensitive whiskers. Some also use high-pitched echo-locating squeaks. Among their primitive characters are the presence of a cloaca, very low and poorly controlled body temperature, and the fact that one of them rears more young in a litter than any other mammal – 32.

That is even bigger than the litter of the Virginia opossum, which cannot exceed thirteen since that is the number of the female's teats.

This group flourished in Africa before Madagascar split away from the eastern flank of the continent. As the millennia passed other kinds of mammals evolved in Africa and many of the ancestral tenrecs disappeared. The only ones that remain on the continent are the otter-shrews, three species of which live in the forests of West Africa. But those that lived in Madagascar were largely free from other mammalian competitors. There they evolved into a range of species which are almost as varied in their specialisms as the marsupials are in Australia.

The most generalised type – and the most shrew-like – is the long-tailed shrew tenrec. It is a little larger than most true shrews but looks remarkably like them and has the same diet, foraging in the undergrowth for insects and other invertebrates. There is an aquatic tenrec, with a long tail and webbed feet, that swims very efficiently, and a rice tenrec that has velvety fur, very small eyes and ears, and closely resembles a mole. The streaked tenrec has several broad reddish stripes running down its body and a prominent crown of long pale hair on its head. It is particularly remarkable because embedded in its fur and scattered

△ *Streaked tenrec, Madagascar*   *European hedgehog with babies* ▷

sparsely over the middle of its back and more densely just behind its neck are quills – hairs that have become very thick, long and sharp. These clearly have a defensive function but the streaked tenrec also uses them for communication. It vibrates those behind its neck which make a rattling squeaking noise that augments its ultrasonic calls. Spinyness has been taken to even greater lengths by a closely-related and rather larger species which has a complete coat of prickles. It is understandably known as a hedgehog tenrec for indeed, at first sight, it seems almost indistinguishable from the common European hedge-hog.

The European hedgehog is not a close cousin of the tenrecs, even though it resembles one of them so closely. Nonetheless it seems to be descended from one of these very ancient groups of insect-eating mammals. Although it is technically classed as an insectivore, it eats many other things as well as insects. In addition to the invertebrates that it finds on the ground – beetles, worms, slugs, earwigs, spiders, millipedes – it will also take birds' eggs, frogs, lizards and even snakes. And if a suburban householder, charmed to see this survivor from the dawn of the age of mammals still fossicking around in the garden, puts down a saucer of bread and milk or minced meat, it will take that too.

With such a wide-ranging diet, hedgehogs can grow to a reasonable size. A big one can be almost a foot long. That, of course, makes it difficult to hide away if it is attacked. The hedgehog, like its distant cousin in Madagascar, has solved that problem by turning the hairs on its back into quills. A hedgehog may have about seven thousand of them, and together they constitute a very effective armour. A band of muscle runs round the margin of this prickly coat. If the hedgehog is alarmed, it contracts this muscle which then acts like the string of a purse, pulling the animal's hind legs towards its shoulders. The hedgehog tucks its head down and the spines on its rear meet those on the back of its head so neatly and tightly that it is difficult at first to see the junction. Certainly dogs are not able to deal with this spiny ball and after pricking their tender noses once or twice they are inclined to leave the hedgehog alone.

Spines could well complicate some aspects of an animal's social life. However, each prickle is controllable to some degree for it has its own small muscle attached to its base. So a female, when she decides the moment has come to mate, is able to pull them all down flat so that they lie close along her back when a male starts to mount her. One might also think that there could be problems when she gave birth to her young, for their prickles are present from an early age. However her infants' skin fits rather loosely around their little bodies and is so swollen with fluid just beneath the surface that the spines do not protrude. The babies therefore do not scratch their mother on their way down from her womb. Immediately after one is born, however, this fluid is rapidly absorbed by the body. As the skin contracts, the spines are forced through it so that a youngster is almost as well protected as its mother from an early age.

Hedgehogs evolved somewhere in Eurasia and, perhaps because of the cold, never managed to spread northwards across the Bering Straits and into the Americas. There, however, another group of the early insect-eaters broadened their diet and grew bigger. They too needed to develop some kind of protection. Instead of prickles they developed bony plates in their skins, covered on their upper surface with horn. It is this armour that has given the whole group their name – the armadillos.

The most perfectly protected of them can roll up even more effectively than a hedgehog. The three-banded armadillo, when curled, is about the size of a grapefruit. The bands that give it its name are three incomplete rings of armour, connected by flexible skin, that encircle the middle of its body. Cup-shaped shields of bone enclose its shoulders and haunches, and it has two small triangular plates, one on the top of its head and the other on its tail. When it rolls up, the

three bands act as a hinge. Head and tail meet and their two triangles fit together to form a rough rectangle so that the whole animal becomes an armoured ball that seems as invulnerable as a coconut. Having closed up, it may remain that way for several minutes until a crack widens to reveal a little beady eye. If it is reassured by what it sees, then the hinge around the waist bends back, the crack opens wide, and four small feet protrude. The animal rights itself and trots away on the tips of its claws like a clockwork toy.

The three-banded is so well armoured that it has little need for any other kind of protection. During the day you may easily find one lying beneath a bush like a fallen fruit. None of the other species, however, takes such risks for none can roll up into such a perfect ball as the three-banded. There are a dozen or so of varying sizes with different numbers of bands around their waists. All are excellent diggers and energetically excavate holes both to find food and to give themselves somewhere safe to spend the day. At one time, there was one as big as a family car. Its armour had no hinge but was a straightforward dome like a mobile igloo. This extraordinary monster perambulated around the plains of Patagonia until quite recently. The last of them, it seems, died only about

Three-banded armadillo, rolled up into a defensive ball △

ten thousand years ago but maybe not before some human beings at least had seen it, for one semi-fossilised carapace has been discovered that appears to have been used by people as a house.

The biggest armadillo alive today is about the size of a large bulldog. It is a formidable digger, excavating huge tunnels into the base of termite hills. You may discover one of these great holes and suspect from the smell inside that its creator is still at the far end but local people will tell you that there is little chance of getting it out. It can dig much faster than you can. This giant, unlike the rest of its family, eats very little other than insects. But it could never achieve its size if it were to pick them up one by one, as a shrew does. It specialises in insects that can be collected by the hundred at a single sitting. It eats almost nothing except colonial insects – ants and termites.

Collecting such insects as these requires special equipment. First you must be

an exceedingly powerful digger to be able to rip apart termite hills – and that the giant armadillo, with its powerful forelegs armed with stout curved claws, certainly is. And second, you have to have an efficient way of gathering up insects in bulk. The giant armadillo does have teeth. Indeed, it has more teeth than almost any other mammal – about a hundred – but they are small, peg-like and degenerate. It seems that, in evolutionary terms, the species is in the process of losing them altogether. Its tongue, however, is long and worm-like and covered with warty tubercles. Its lower jaw also holds enormous glands that secrete great quantities of a particularly glue-like saliva. With this coating its tongue, the giant armadillo can lick up hundreds of termites at a time.

Other armoured ant and termite eaters live in Africa and Asia. These, the pangolins, protect themselves with armour of a different kind – roughly triangular horny plates that overlap one another like the scales on a fir cone. The pangolins are so specialised that they can now eat nothing else but ants and termites for their jaws have lost all their teeth and are little more than a curving tube housing a very long tongue. Several species of them spend their lives in trees and clamber about with the aid of a long grasping tail. The biggest of them, however, the giant African pangolin, which has a body two and a half feet long and a tail of a similar length, doesn't risk climbing and lives entirely on the ground.

A pangolin in search of a meal opens a termite nest with a slash of the claws

◁ *Giant armadillo, Brazil*   *Malayan pangolin, Java* △

on its front legs, and pokes its curved snout inside. Angry termites will swarm out to defend their colony but the pangolin is little affected. It presses its horny scales firmly against one another, it keeps the lids of its eyes, which are particularly thick, tightly shut and it closes its nostrils with special muscles. It then protrudes a long black tongue which is liberally anointed with a sticky spittle that pours from an enormous salivary gland housed in its chest. This tongue snakes into the wrecked galleries of the ants' nest, collects the insects and, flicking in and out, carries them back to its mouth. There they are immediately swallowed and mashed up by the horny lining of the muscular stomach. In this fashion, the giant African pangolin can consume as many as 200,000 insects in a single night.

Tooth-loss and tongue development has been taken to similar extremes in South America. There is a giant ant-eating species here too, even bigger than the giant pangolin. It stands over a metre high at the shoulders. Its curving snout alone is almost two feet long and its bowed forelegs are so powerful that even a jaguar would not be able to escape its embrace. Instead of armour, its body is covered with a coarse shaggy fur which, on its spine, stands upright forming a crest. On the upper and lower surface of its tail, this hair is so long that the tail looks like a huge banner. The giant anteater lives on the grassy plains of South America from the Guyanas down to northern Argentina. Here on the open savannahs, mud fortresses built by termites stud the ground like tombstones. The giant anteater spends most of the day asleep, lying in a patch of tall grass and sheltered from the sun by its gigantic tail which it folds over itself. When darkness comes, it starts to shamble about its territory looking for food. It tends to avoid termites, leaf-cutting ants or army ants, all of which have castes of specialised soldier with very effective jaws. Instead it prefers carpenter ants which are less ferocious. Even then, a giant anteater seldom stays long enough at any one feeding site to take more than a hundred or so insects. It then moves away before the battalions of the colony's soldiers pour out of their breached fortress to attack their enemy in numbers.

There is a smaller version of the giant anteater, similar in shape but with short fur and less than half the size, which not only tackles terrestrial colonies of termites but climbs up into trees, using its tail to give it a grip, to tackle them there as well. This is the tamandua. Its tail is naked and grasping. The animal is quite discriminating in what it feeds on. Leaf cutting ants are very common in the South American forest, but they have jaws like scissors with which to cut leaf segments and they use them unhesitatingly on anything that interferes with them. The tamandua avoids them. Neither does it like army ants which also have

formidable jaws and can tear a scorpion to pieces. Like the giant, it prefers the much less aggressive tree termites whose workers munch rotting wood and have soft and succulent bodies.

And there is a third South American anteater – a pygmy. This is less than a foot long and spends its entire life in trees. Its fur is soft and golden yellow. It sleeps throughout the day, curled into a small ball and at nights clambers myopically around the trees picking off ants from the branches. It seldom does so for more than about four hours – and then needs a rest. Should you find one, the best it can do to defend itself, is to rear back on its hind legs, its tail wound round a branch to give itself some support, and wave its front legs at you, showing off its little curved claws.

The truth is that ants and termites, as food, leave a lot to be desired. They are not very nourishing. Their crunchy external skeletons are virtually indigestible. So animals that eat nothing else do not have much energy to spare. They spend as little as possible of it on heating their bodies and have the lowest body temperature of any land-living placental mammals – 32.7° C. They spend

Giant anteater, Brazil △

fifteen hours out of every twenty-four asleep. The females can only produce one young at a time. The pygmy anteater doesn't have enough energy to power lightning defensive action. Even the giant anteater at full gallop can be out-run by a man. None of them could be accused of having a dazzling, sparkling intelligence. But having evolved the apparatus necessary to collect ants and termites, they have lost the ability their remote ancestors once had to eat a wider range of invertebrate food. The price of adopting a specialised diet can be high.

△ *Pygmy anteater*

3

CHISELLERS

No animal can create food for itself. Only plants, fuelled by sunshine, can combine water, carbon dioxide and a few nutrients and so produce sugars and starches. As a consequence, all animals are ultimately dependent upon plants for their food. For the first mammals, the insectivores, that dependence was indirect. They ate small animals which themselves ate plants. But other early mammals began to eat plants directly.

Plants do not surrender their tissues passively and some they protect with special care. Their seeds are particularly precious to them and they are also particularly worth stealing for each is packed with sufficient energy-rich food to enable the seedling to build the leaves, and sometimes even a supporting stem, that it must have to create food for itself. The first birds must have started to steal seeds at a very early stage in evolutionary history for conifers began to protect their seeds within clusters of specially toughened leaves, their cones. Later, flowering plants created other kinds of defences, strengthening the coats of their seeds. Some went even further and equipped each seed with a thick woody shell. One group of mammals, in turn, responded by developing powerful armour-piercing tools – chisel-shaped front teeth, two in the upper jaw and two in the lower. These creatures were the ancestors of today's rodents.

Cutting through woody material blunts any tool. The front teeth of a rodent, however, are self-sharpening. The layer of enamel on the front face of each is harder than the dentine behind it which makes up the body of the tooth, so as they grind together, upper on lower, the dentine is worn away more quickly. That leaves the enamel layer as a cutting edge, projecting slightly proud of the dentine. But even this hard thin blade is ground away eventually, so gnawing inevitably wears the teeth down – in some cases by several

◁ *Pygmy anteater*

millimetres a week. To compensate for this loss, a rodent's front incisors have open roots and continue to grow throughout their owner's life.

Such carpentry inevitably produces a considerable amount of shavings. To avoid swallowing such indigestible mouthfuls, rodents have a gap between the front gnawing incisors and the molars at the back of the jaw with which they will grind up the seeds once the shell has been removed. That space allows them to get rid of the shavings produced by the incisors.

Many rodents are ready to tackle a seed just as soon as it is mature enough to be worth eating. Squirrels, with sharp nails on their toes to give them a firm grip, can scamper up vertical tree trunks and run along branches at great speed. Most species are sufficiently small and lightweight that they can reach the very tips of branches to collect seeds just as soon as they are worth eating.

Some climbing rodents, however, are even smaller than squirrels. One of the smallest is the tiny harvest mouse. Its head and body are a mere three inches long (70 mm). It has no need to jump in order to reach its food whether in hedgerows, where some still live, or in the wheat fields where, in the days before industrialised harvesting, many of them made their homes. They can simply reach out from stem to stem to collect their seeds. To enable them to do that with

complete security, they have gripping tails which they wrap firmly round the plant stems. There are no tree holes in wheat fields or reed beds so these elegant little mice have to create their own homes, weaving shredded grass leaves between growing stems to create globular nests.

In spite of all these busy collectors, some seeds do, of course, fall to the

◁ *Harvest mouse in its nest*   *Harvest mouse feeding* △

ground. But here another range of rodents awaits them. In South American forests, the agouti is particularly assiduous. Some of the nuts that fall to the ground here are so stoutly armoured that even a man with a machete finds it very hard, if not impossible, to crack them. But none of them defeats the agouti. It chisels a small rectangular hole in the side of the shell and then using its lower incisors as spatulae, extracts the protein-rich kernel.

Many trees produce huge numbers of nuts at the same time. That is another way of increasing the chances that some will germinate. The permanent population of seed-eaters around a tree cannot consume every nut in such a sudden glut. But the agouti has a way of dealing with that too. It gathers them up and dashes off to bury them in special places all over the forest floor. It then comes back, days or even weeks later, and reclaims them. Of course, it seldom if ever remembers where it placed every single nut so a few, eventually, germinate and the parent tree has managed, after all, not only to produce another generation but has succeeded in having some of that generation planted beyond the parental shade. There is one final twist to this story of interdependence. The Brazil nut tree now encloses its seeds in an armoured pod of such impregnability that unless an agouti opens it initially, the seeds themselves will not germinate at all. So now the Brazil nut tree is totally dependent on what was once its arch enemy.

△ *Agouti, Paraguay*   *Kangaroo rat leaping near its burrow, Texas* ▷

The agouti is active during the day but many rodents make their collections under the cover of darkness to avoid as far as possible any threatening predators. Even so, owls have a sense of hearing so acute that they can locate the slightest rustle and pounce with lethal accuracy. Foxes, weasels and cats of many kinds prowl through the night-time forest, so a rodent should spend as little time as possible unprotected out in the open, day or night.

The African pouched rat when it ventures out of its hole, rushes around picking up everything that looks vaguely edible. Without examining what it has found, it hurriedly crams it into huge pouches in its cheeks. When these are so full that its whole face bulges, it sprints back to its hole and to safety. Once there, in a more leisurely way, it unloads its pouches and inspects each find, one at a time. It is quite a big creature. Discounting its tail, its body can be up to 17 inches long. Its cheek pouches are correspondingly capacious and can contain several dozen morsels of one kind and another. And such is its hurry that individuals have been known to pick up not only nuts, beans and tubers, but coins, keys, and marbles.

In the desert regions of the south-western United States, seeds are only available for a very short time of the year, so rodents that live there, the

kangaroo rats, collect every seed they can find and take them down into their burrows. They then store them in special larders to keep themselves supplied through the harsh months when food above ground is very scarce. They defend these stores from other rats by foot drumming – thumping a rapid tattoo on the ground with their back feet. If that doesn't work, they kick sand at the intruder.

There are other ways of storing food for the winter. Marmots, rodents the size of large puppies that live in the European Alps, do so within their own bodies as fat. Their feeding season is a brief one. On the higher mountain slopes, the vegetation may only be free of snow for a mere five months of the year, so during this brief summer the marmots feed intensively, gathering not only the seeds that appear in the last few weeks, but flowers and leaves.

Marmots live in families of up to twenty individuals – a female and her mate,

△ *Marmot collecting bedding for the winter*

together with one or two young that were born at the beginning of summer, and sometimes one or two of the female's sisters. Each family has its own pasture and defends it by marking stones around the boundaries with a smear of a smelly oil from glands on their cheeks. If a neighbour recklessly ignores this signal and seems intent on trespass, one or two of the owning family will drive it away, gnashing their front teeth and calling loudly.

By the end of the summer the adults in the marmot family will have accumulated substantial reserves of fat and may be almost 50 per cent heavier than they were at the beginning of the season. Last year's young have grown fast and are now fully adult. Shortly after mating, the dominant female in the group begins to behave in an odd manner, attacking her young in a seemingly very ill-tempered way. The young females become so stressed that even though they might have mated, they seldom become pregnant and if they have conceived they will abort. The advantage that comes from the dominant female behaving in this manner will not become apparent for some weeks.

As the first snows begin to fall, the fat marmots retire to their family hole. They block its entrance and retreat to a deep chamber and there they curl up in one large huddle. The snow lies thick on the slopes above and the marmots switch off most of their bodily processes and fall into a deep sleep. They hibernate. Their breathing slows to two or three breaths a minute. Their body temperature drops from 36°C to a mere five. If they were to cool any farther, they would die. They are fuelled entirely by their fat reserves.

But this year's babies have virtually none. They have not had sufficient time to accumulate any. They are dependent on the adults to maintain that crucial five degrees above freezing and they snuggle up close to their mother to share her warmth. Now the reason why the dominant female inhibited breeding by her juniors becomes evident. If there were more youngsters, there would not be enough warmth to sustain them for the six months that they will have to spend in this chilly dormitory.

Beavers do not have to fall into such a deep sleep. They have found a way of maintaining a supply of food throughout the winter, even though the woods around them are deep in snow and their lake is ice-bound. They use a lake as a larder.

A pair, setting up home for the first time, selects a valley with a small stream running down it. Across this, they construct a dam. They are big, hefty animals with bodies that can be four feet long, not counting their tail, and they have immense chisel-sharp incisor teeth. They cut down substantial trees and haul

Marmots in the summer, Switzerland ▷▷

them into place across the stream-bed. They shift boulders and heap them along-side the logs. They plaster mud on the upstream side. On the downstream face, they lay more tree trunks, placing them upright against the dam wall to prevent it being pushed downwards by the weight of water. As the dam rises and the lake behind it grows, the dam may need to be extended laterally. Soon the beavers are likely to have exhausted the supply of suitable trees nearby and are having to travel long distances to find them. They go up the valley above the dam. There they build canals down to the lake so that they can fell logs and float them all the way down to the dam. A pair will maintain the same dam year after year, extend-ing its width and so increasing the size of the lake. Some dams may eventually be a hundred yards long.

At one side or, even better, on a small hillock that the rising waters of the lake have turned into an island, they build their lodge. They begin by excavating a tunnel that starts underwater and opens near the margin of the lake. Then they heap mud, boulders and branches on top of the land entrance. As they add more, so they hollow out the inside of the mound until they have created a large dome-shaped chamber, roofed with rushes, with a tunnel in its floor that leads

70

△ *Beaver felling a tree*

down to the lake. Now the owners are very safe indeed, for they can get in and out of the water without being seen. They feed on bark and the nutritious tissues that lie just beneath it, together with rushes, leaves and other vegetation which they find in and around their lake. As they swim, propelling themselves with their webbed feet, all you are likely to see of them is the top of their heads just above water and a V-shaped ripple spreading across the smooth surface of their lake. If they catch sight of you, they may take fright. They suddenly smack the surface of the water with their broad scaly tail, making a loud crack that warns other members of their family of the danger you may represent. Then they dive. They can easily remain submerged for five minutes and are said to be able to do so for almost a quarter of an hour. But it may be even longer than that before their heads reappear on the surface of the water for they will be safe inside their lodge, having swum across to it and entered it unseen.

As autumn approaches, the beavers continue to cut down leafy branches in the surrounding woodland and feed on them. Some, however, they haul into the lake. There they submerge them. These are their winter rations which the near-freezing water will keep relatively fresh and green. As autumn turns to

71

A beaver dam, Argentina △

winter, the temperature of the water falls until eventually, ice spreads across its surface. Snow blankets the forest. The mud, rushes and branches forming the roof of the beavers' lodge freezes solid and it becomes as hard as concrete.

The aspen and the willow around the lake are now leafless, but some of their branches, with leaves attached, are lying in the cold store on the lake bottom. The beavers, unseen by the outside world, leave their lodge and swim down to collect fresh supplies. The days get shorter and shorter. It is always pitch black in the lodge and very little light filters through the roof of ice that covers their underwater larder. Nonetheless, they maintain a daily rhythm, just as they did in summer, alternating activity with sleep. As winter progresses, the daylight that cues this rhythm becomes dimmer and shorter. Eventually, the beavers become largely impervious to the diurnal cycle of light and darkness outside. They work to their own clocks. By mid-winter, they may remain continuously active for as long as twenty hours at a stretch before they reckon that the time has come for a sleep. So beavers may have a year which has fewer days in it than that of nearly all other mammals.

△ *Beaver repairing its dam*

We wanted to watch them and see just what they did at this time, so one winter we carefully bored a narrow hole through the roof of a lodge and inserted an optical cable carrying infra-red light with a special miniature camera on the end. What we saw was a surprise. The beavers certainly were active for unusually long periods, but there were more than beavers living in the lodge. Several muskrats had found their way to the underwater entrance and were now living alongside the beavers.

Muskrats are also excellent swimmers but smaller than beavers and about the size of rabbits. They burrow into river-banks and make mounds like smaller versions of the beavers' lodge. They keep small holes open in the ice so that they can leave the lake at night throughout the winter and go in search of food in the countryside. To prevent these holes from freezing over, they plug them with wads of vegetation which they change daily. But they do not maintain a well-stocked refrigerator like the prudent hard-working beavers. We watched muskrats in the lodge taking a not inconsiderable share of the beavers'

73

Beaver stocking its winter store, △
North America

food. The rightful owners, fumbling their way around in the pitch darkness and the cold, seemed totally unaware that they had uninvited guests at their table.

Beavers, spending all their lives beside or in their lakes, are always close to safety. Few other rodents are so lucky. Belding's ground squirrels live in holes, but they have to venture some considerable distance from them in order to collect their food — seeds and flower heads, supplemented by insects and birds' eggs if they can find them. Belding's ground squirrels live in colonies several hundred strong in North America's Sierra Nevada. They have an early warning system. Some adults are always on guard, sitting upright, scanning the land and sky for hunters such as badgers or eagles, coyotes or weasels. If they spot danger they give loud alarm calls and immediately all the foraging squirrels within many yards sprint for cover. But sentry duty is not shared by all. It is a dangerous job. Many more sentries lose their lives to predators than do those who heed the warnings but never give them. Males and young under a year old seldom take on the job. It is also rare for females without young to do so. Most of the watchers are mature females with young. Matrons in this society, it seems, are more prepared than anyone else in the family to give their lives on behalf of the next generation.

The safest policy for burrowers, of course, is never to come above ground at all and a few rodents don't. Mole-rats manage to find *all* the food they need

74

△ *Muskrat, North America*

Ground squirrel on sentry duty, ▷
North America

underground. Nine different species of them live in the drier parts of southern Africa, the Middle East and south-eastern Europe. In these areas some plants manage to survive by storing both food and water in huge swollen roots and tubers. The mole-rats steal these food stores. Finding them, however, is a major problem, for such plants in dry country are usually widely separated.

But mole-rats are very industrious and efficient tunnellers for they use their front teeth not so much as chisels as mechanical excavators. Their incisors project so far beyond the mouth that their owner's furry lips close behind them. As a consequence, mole-rats manage to avoid swallowing any of the soil and sand that they excavate. One species, in order to make doubly sure, has been seen to hold part of the husk of a tuber behind its teeth and in front of its mouth so that it served as a face-mask. The wear on the incisors as they cut through the soil is particularly heavy, so it is essential that they grow fast and continuously. Consequently, the mole-rat's incisors have extremely long open roots that extend far back along the jaw, even beyond the roots of their cheek teeth. All the cheek teeth have to do, of course, is to chew up vegetables, and that, by comparison, is a very easy job so long roots are not necessary.

△ *Damaraland mole rat, Namibia*

As the mole-rats dig out soil, they kick it backwards. When some quantity has accumulated, they go into reverse, like a London tube train that has reached its terminus. They push the pile back down the tunnel and then along a branch line until they reach a vertical shaft where they can kick it up to the surface. There it forms a pile like that made by a true mole.

Neither sight nor smell can give the mole-rats any clue as to the where-abouts of a life-saving tuber. All they can do is to dig at random and hope that they will bump into one. Some of their tunnels may run for half a mile. When a mole-rat does at last find a root, it gnaws at the juicy flesh – but not too deeply. That could kill the plant. If it does not do so immediately, it could be the cause of the plant's death in the next dry season since it has been robbed of all its reserves. So before even the majority of a root is eaten, a mole-rat is likely to leave it and tunnel away to look for more. That way, there may be several permanent feeding stations in its underground network.

Most species of these underground rodents are either solitary or live in small groups. They still have tiny eyes, but these are sightless. Their legs are very short, since they are only needed to push their bodies along the tunnels. Their ears, which are simple holes, are buried deep in the fur. Their nostrils are small and can be closed tight during digging. In fact, most mole-rats look like furry sausages.

One species, however, is more extremely and dramatically adapted to the underground life than any other – the naked mole-rat. It has lost all its fur. Keeping warm underground, where the temperature varies very little, is not a major problem in hot desert regions and a coat is unnecessary. Unlike furred mole-rats, the naked species lives in huge colonies of up to eighty individuals. The reason for such numbers is clear. Food plants in the parched country in-habited by mole-rats are so rare that a solitary individual would have little chance of finding one by itself. A whole army of workers is needed to tunnel through the ground and locate the plants. They work in teams, one at the front cutting into the earth, several behind, kicking the loosened soil along the tun-nel, and one remaining close to the exit shaft to kick it out.

Before long a colony creates a complex network of tunnels extending over a wide area. Special chambers are excavated which serve as larders and latrines and there is a central nesting chamber shared by all. In this underground city, the mole-rats are very safe indeed. The only real gaps in their defences are the open vertical shafts beside the spoil tips. Snakes can slide down them. If they do, they meet with a very determined and effective defence. The worker mole-rats attack them, snorting ferociously. If one manages to sink its incisors into the snake's flesh, it often refuses to let go. Instead it reverses at full speed, dragging the snake along the tunnel where it is bitten unremittingly by many others until it dies.

Only one female in the mole-rat colony is fertile. She seldom strays far from the communal nesting chamber. Here, every eighty days, she produces huge litters. Usually these contain around a dozen or so, but one female has been recorded as giving birth to thirty-three young – the biggest litter produced by any mammal other than a marsupial.

A few individuals are intermediate in size between the small workers and the giant queen. These take almost no part in tunnelling or any other work. They are of both sexes. The males will copulate with the queen and both they and the females will assist in raising the young that she produces, bringing food to them and allowing them to feed on their faeces. That, it seems, is essential in order that the young shall acquire the bacteria they need in their guts to enable them to digest their vegetable food. The females in this group are sterile, but not permanently so. Should the queen die, the biggest and strongest of them will start to grow. If it is not already clear which one this is, there are fights which may continue for several months. When the winner has finally been established, she

begins to change. Her teats start to enlarge. Even more remarkably, she develops a bigger abdomen by increasing the size of her lumbar vertebrae and so creating more space within her body for litters. Then she takes over breeding duties.

So why does she not do so earlier? What prevents her from settling in to a nest chamber of her own and producing her own babies? It seems likely that the reigning female – the queen of this underground kingdom – secretes a special chemical substance, a pheromone that inhibits the sexual development of all other females. They absorb it involuntarily either by direct contact with the queen's naked skin, or from the urine she deposits in the communal latrine. She also bullies them mercilessly.

There is one further caste within this group of lazy intermediate-sized individuals that has only recently been recognised. This is the disperser. Like others of its size, the disperser does little digging or other work. But unlike them, dispersers – which are both male and female – are sexually primed. Yet they show no interest in breeding with the queen or with any other member of the colony. During the night, both male and female dispersers will leave their underground city and travel overland in search of a new one. Entering a strange

◁ *Naked mole-rats fighting*   *Queen mole-rat suckling her young* △

colony is not easy for them. All mole-rats have a very acute and discriminating sense of smell. An intruder is quickly recognised. Once inside a new tunnel system, the disperser makes for the communal nest. As it enters there is pandemonium. Dozens of naked bodies writhe together in a ferocious scrum. Curved incisor teeth stab in the darkness. If the disperser manages to survive this ordeal for only a short time, it acquires enough of the new colony's smell to conceal its original one. The fighting comes to an end and the newcomer settles in. If it is lucky, it may in due course become one of its breeders.

The reproductive system practised by naked mole-rats is a highly specialised one. No other rodent, indeed no other mammal, does anything similar. Rodents, however, are very versatile and varied in their sexual habits. Some are promiscuous, some polygamous, and some monogamous.

Few copulations have raised as much speculation as that of one particular rodent, the porcupine. The African species has quills banded with black and white, some of which are nearly two feet long. If anything interferes with it – whether a lion or merely an inquisitive human being – it will issue a series of warnings. First, it erects its quills into a huge halo that doubles its apparent size and makes it look very fearsome indeed. Then it shakes a group of specialised hollow quills on

the end of its tail, which make an ominous rattling noise. Finally, as an indication that it is getting very angry, it stamps its hind feet. If all this is not enough to deter a stranger, then the porcupine will suddenly spin round and rush backwards with such speed that its attacker may be seriously stabbed. Some of its quills are only loosely attached and may stay in the wounds they make. It is not uncommon to see young lions with porcupine quills in their muzzles. They are unlikely to attack a porcupine again.

The effectiveness of the porcupine's defences, however, does raise the question of how male and female porcupine get close enough to one another in order to mate. Understandably, each partner needs some considerable reassurance that the other is favourably disposed. They approach cautiously and begin to groom one another around the head where their hair, though coarse, is not spiny. This behaviour continues as they circle one another and call. Then the male moves behind the female and parts the long backward pointing quills on either side of her haunches. She erects the quills on her back and raises her tail. The male then stands on his hind legs and cautiously advances until the underside of her tail is supporting his belly – and intromission is safely achieved.

Interestingly enough, once having successfully negotiated the hazards of such congress, a pair seems only too happy to repeat it. Although the female only becomes fertile every 35 days or so, the male mounts most evenings and actually copulates on most if not all of those occasions. Perhaps this consolidates their relationship with one another. If that is the case, then they are the only mammal to do so apart from some of the primates.

Flying squirrels are entirely promiscuous. Both male and female, during the breeding season, attempt to mate with as many partners as they can. A pair will court by prancing together. Then they copulate. After doing so, the male seals the female's genital opening with a plug of congealed seminal fluids the size and shape of a cigarette end. This is an attempt to ensure that the female will bear his offspring and not those of a later partner. But his strategy often fails. The flying squirrel penis is shaped like a corkscrew and the next male to come along uses it to remove the plug and then copulates himself.

A Californian species of deer mouse, in contrast, has bonds between male and female that are very long lasting. Indeed, if for some reason a male abandons his mate half way through her pregnancy, she may not even give birth at all but will resorb the little foetuses. This attachment between the pair continues through gestation to the birth itself. As a pregnant female starts to produce her young in her underground burrow, the male grooms her and helps in the

◁ *Cape porcupine, Kalahari, South Africa*

delivery of her babies. When they arrive, he takes even more trouble over grooming and cleaning them than she does. He brings food to mother and babies, and when the female goes out to feed for herself, he crouches over the youngsters to keep them warm.

Mara couples help one another. They live on the open pampas of Patagonia. The mara is related to the agouti of the rain forest but here on the open pampas, it has grown to the size of a spaniel and has long legs to give it the speed to out-run a fox. They are monogamous, and each pair usually lives by itself and keeps away from others, perhaps because the vegetation of the pampas is relatively poor and will not support many individuals in one area. But when the breeding season comes, as many as a dozen pairs will collaborate and run a creche.

Creating suitable premises for a creche is not easy out on the open pampas. Female maras are capable of digging holes if necessary but, if they can, they adapt one that already exists. An excavation made by a burrowing owl or an armadillo in search of a meal could provide them with just what they want. Once it has been enlarged to the necessary size, no adult mara will enter it again that season. Each female gives birth to her young at the entrance of the creche. There are up to three babies and they totter unaided into the shelter. The mother then departs. When she returns, she comes to the entrance and calls with a shrill whistle.

82

△ *Deer mouse transporting her young, North America*

A mara creche, Argentina ▷
Mara suckling her young ▷

Twenty or thirty hungry infants may rush out, but she will only accept her own, and leads them away while the others go back into the tunnel and the safety of the creche. While this is going on, her mate stands on guard ready to give warnings of predators such as foxes or snakes. If another pair approaches wishing to feed their own young, the guardian male will send them away with a call, and the newly arrived female will have to wait until the earlier female has finished suckling. Only then can the next mother summon her own babies. So the young of the whole group are under almost continuous protection.

Perhaps the most remarkable aspect of rodent reproduction, however, is its record-breaking productivity. Rats and mice in human habitation, protected from the vagaries of weather outside, and presented by humanity with a never-ending supply of food can overrun an establishment within weeks. But plagues of rodents can also occur independently of mankind. The most famous is that generated periodically by the lemmings.

The Norwegian lemming lives in the tundra and birch woods of the Scandinavian mountains. It is a dumpy mouse-sized creature with thick brown fur patterned with black. In any population, there are more females than males and it is they that form the stable social groups — mother, sisters, daughters and

granddaughters, all living together. The males are wanderers. One of them will venture down a tunnel to visit these all-female groups but initially he is not welcomed. The females set upon him and bite him so cruelly that he may well retreat. The females thus ensure that the father of their young will not only be lustful but strong. If the male is persistent and stoical enough to withstand this onslaught, he is allowed to take up temporary residence. Then he copulates with all the females, one after another.

The reproductive ability of a female lemming is phenomenal. She gives birth a mere sixteen days after copulation and may produce up to a dozen young. Each of these grows so fast that it is sexually mature before it is three weeks old. Meanwhile the first female has mated again and will produce yet another litter within a month of giving birth to her first. If there is sufficient food and space, she can breed throughout the year. Not surprisingly therefore, as the vegetation on which lemmings live increases through the spring and summer, the population grows rapidly. By the beginning of autumn, it may be two hundred times what it was in the spring. Even allowing for great losses in the following winter when conditions are harder and food is more difficult to find, this process cannot go on indefinitely. After about four or five years, there is not enough food to withstand cropping by such huge numbers and the population suddenly crashes.

But every thirty or forty years or so in the autumn there is a population explosion on an altogether different scale. Its causes are still not properly understood. Suddenly from the upland forests of Scandinavia, a great tide of lemmings emerges and starts to flow down towards the valleys, advancing by as much as ten miles a day. The animals invade cultivated fields destroying the crops. They swarm into gardens and houses. They tumble down wells where their rotting bodies foul the water. In 1970, on a hundred and twenty mile stretch of road, 20,000 were killed by cars.

The lemmings, as they search frantically for food, become very aggressive. Indeed they are so ferocious that they will attack creatures many time their size – including human beings. Fights may break out between them as they rush wildly onwards searching for new territory and more food.

If they reach a river, the pressure of those advancing from behind may force the leaders to take to the water. They are very competent swimmers. Their dense buoyant fur causes them to ride high in the water with their backs fully exposed, so the surface of a river may appear to be clotted with them. The animals are able to avoid swimming in circles for they can orientate themselves by

◁ *Norwegian lemming*

distant hills on the horizon. Even so they cannot know how far they have to go to reach the opposite bank. Equally they cannot be aware, when they arrive at the edge of the sea, that there is no land within possible reach. Nonetheless, they set off. There is a nineteenth century record that a steamer off Trondheim took a quarter of an hour to pass through a vast swarm of them. Such sights gave rise to myth.

In the Middle Ages it was believed that swarms of lemming, appearing apparently from nowhere, had fallen from the skies. They were, some claimed, the coagulation of foul matter in the clouds. In the far North some Inuit people still call them 'creatures from outer space'. Some people said that they swam out to sea because they were attempting to reach their ancient home in the lost continent of Atlantis. Others, more famously and indeed even recently, maintained that the lemming, when its numbers got too great, deliberately committed suicide.

The fact is, however, that this behaviour can result in the species expanding its range very considerably. The migration that took place in northern Finland in 1902 led to the establishment of lemming colonies as far away as the coast of the Baltic Sea a hundred miles or so away from their previous territory. Those colonies only flourished for a few years, but such behaviour could clearly be important for the survival of a species living in a part of the world where the climate varies consistently over long periods. In recent centuries in the Arctic, glaciers have advanced and retreated, snow-fields appeared and disappeared, and land that once was once frozen and barren has again become habitable. If such changes become long lasting, the lemmings will be among the first to discover it and so will be able to rapidly take control of new territory.

A dozing three-toed sloth, South America ▷

4

PLANT PREDATORS

You could be forgiven for not recognising it as an animal. It looks like a bundle of greyish withered leaves hanging high in a tree in the South American rain forest. You may watch it for an hour without seeing any sign of movement. Thump the tree trunk and still it may not shift. Even a gunshot is unlikely to produce any reaction. Yet the bundle is indeed a living animal. It is a three-toed sloth and its torpor, verging so close to immobility, is the price it pays for living almost entirely on leaves.

Leaves are extremely poor food. Their liquid sap does contain a little nutriment but most of their bulk is made up of cellulose and that is extraordinarily indigestible. No mammal has a stomach that, unaided, can break it down. The only living organisms that can do so are bacteria and the sloth, like all mammals that eat leaves in quantity, maintains flourishing cultures of bacteria in its digestive system. But even with their help, leaves take a long time to digest and produce little energy for their bulk. The best that can be said for mature leaves as food, is that there are plenty of them.

The three-toed sloth copes with the shortcomings of its diet by being extremely sparing in its expenditure of energy. It can cling to its tree without any effort whatsoever. Its toes, three on both fore and hind legs, end in curved hooks which it latches on to a branch. No muscular grip is required. If a hunter in these forests shoots a sloth, it will still hang suspended even though dead, and the hunter, if he wants the body, will have to climb up the tree and unhook it.

Even when the sloth decides to move, it does so with minimum effort. The slim ribbon-like muscles of its legs are relatively feeble and incapable of moving its limbs with either speed or force. It spends little of its energy heating its body and keeps it only marginally warmer than the tepid moisture-laden air of the rain forest, allowing it to chill when the weather gets cold and warm as it gets hotter. When, occasionally, it eats, it chews its leaves with slow, deliberate champing movements. Its digestive processes are so slow that it usually only defecates once a week and may retain a meal in its stomach for up to a month. Its eyes are small and far from acute; it shows little sign of being able to hear anything that is going on around it and it seldom makes any sound itself, except low moans during courtship. It sleeps for about eighteen hours in twenty-four.

One might think, therefore, that the sloth, condemned by its diet to live in a dim, muffled, slow-motion world, has a deprived life. Yet the fact is that it is very successful – if success is to be measured in terms of the density of population. Although anyone travelling through these forests seldom sees a sloth, a systematic search in any given patch of trees reveals surprisingly large numbers of them. And they have few enemies. Jaguars, even if they succeed in climbing the trees, cannot reach below the branch to grapple with them. The sloth's only regular predator, it seems, are harpy eagles. Their basic diet is monkeys and opossums but they will grab a sloth if they spot one that has incautiously clambered into the exposed crown of a forest tree to warm itself in the sun.

The labour-saving habit of hanging upside down has led to other adaptations in the three-toed sloth. So that it may see where it is going – when it does

◁ *Two-toed sloth, Brazil*

decide to go somewhere – it has developed an extremely long neck that contains eight or in some individuals, nine vertebrae. Most mammals have only seven. This allows it to twist its head around through 270 degrees and peer forward without difficulty even though it is upside down. And the hair tracts on its body do not run from its spine and along its flanks to the belly, as is the case with virtually all other mammals. Instead they part along the midline of its stomach and run towards its backbone.

The sloth is so lethargic and so careless of its toilet that it has become a minor ecosystem all on its own. Its hairs have grooves running along their length which provide lodgement for a variety of unicellular algae. These flourish and dwindle according to conditions so, in the rainy season, three-toed sloths turn green. These algae provide food for flightless moths and ticks. Beetles also live permanently in this slowly perambulating shaggy blanket.

The three-toed sloth has a relative living in the South American forests that has reacted in the same way to the problems of leaf-eating and taken to a life of lethargy For this reason it too is called a sloth, though how closely related it is to the three-toed is debatable. It has only two toes on its forelegs and three on its hind, but by and large it is not quite so slothful. It has a less mobile neck, is about 25 percent heavier, eats a greater variety of vegetation and ranges more widely in search of it.

The sloths' way of dealing with the dietary shortcomings of leaves, it must be said, are eccentric. Most leaf-eaters have adopted a radically different solution. Instead of relapsing into indolence, they lead relatively active lives but pay for it by eating a very great deal. This was the method adopted by one of the first mammals to take to this diet when forests of broad-leaved trees began to spread through the world around fifty-five million years ago, soon after the disappearance of the dinosaurs. The direct descendants of these pioneers, little changed in form, are still following the same policy. These are the tapirs.

The Brazilian tapir is about the size of a donkey, but much more heavily built and without a hairy coat. It feeds throughout the day and the night. It has two kinds of teeth. Those in the front, the incisors, are chisel-shaped and are used to snip off leaves. Those at the back, the molars, which are separated from the incisors by a toothless gap in the jaw, are flat and ridged on top. These grind the leaves, physically breaking down the cellulose to release the nutritious cell contents. Each mouthful, having been thoroughly chewed, then passes through the stomach and along the hind gut where the tapir, like the sloth, keeps colonies of

bacteria and other micro-organisms. They continue the attack on the cellulose by biochemical means.

Tapirs have nostrils that are elongated into diminutive trunks and with these they sniff out and identify the leaves they prefer. And while they seem prepared to eat most things – including fruits and nuts if they can find them – they have to be careful about which kind of leaves they swallow. Leaves are valuable property as far as a plant is concerned and many species have developed ways to prevent them being stolen. Some surround them or coat them with sharp spines. Others load them with poisons. The tapir, however, has ways of dealing with these defences. Its tongue is long, muscular and mobile and a tapir can curl it round most spines to reach the leaves. They can even deal with some of the poisons. They travel regularly to special places in the forest where there are clays containing kaolin. Kaolin has the invaluable quality of absorbing and binding other chemicals, thus making them inactive. We ourselves take it as a remedy for upset stomachs. The tapirs rake off considerable quantities of the clay with their teeth or forefeet and swallow it to get the same effect.

Tracking a tapir is not difficult. It is an excellent swimmer, spending much of its time close to water and a good place to look for its footprints is in the sand

Brazilian tapir in rain-forest △

at the edge of a forest river. They are unmistakable. There are four toes on the front feet and three on the back. Even in the muddy ground away from the rivers, the prints are easy to identify. But the animal itself, in spite of being by far the biggest inhabitant of these rain forests, is surprisingly difficult to detect in the shady gloom.

You may first become aware of its presence, as it stands quietly feeding maybe twenty yards away, when you hear the snap and rustle of leaves being plucked. The animal is likely to be by itself, unless it is a mature female in which case it may be accompanied by its calf. The youngster will be even more difficult to spot, for if it is within a few weeks of being born it will have a coat dappled with alternating stripes and spots that conceals it very effectively.

There are three species of tapir in South and Central America. There is a fourth in South-East Asia which is known as the Malayan tapir, though it is also found in Sumatra to the south and Thailand and Burma to the north. Until quite recently it also lived in Borneo. It differs from its South American cousins chiefly in its colour, for while the front part of its body and its hind legs are black, its rear half is greyish white, a strange piebald coloration that is said to help the animal's concealment by breaking up its outline.

The forests of South-east Asia are also inhabited by another forest browser with a very ancient history. Today its main stronghold is Sumatra, but there are relict populations in Borneo, the Malay peninsula and perhaps Burma. Like the tapirs, it is donkey-sized and has a reduced number of toes, three on both front and back legs. It is the hairy rhinoceros. Only about three hundred still exist to-day. It seems likely that it digests its food in much the same way as the tapir does.

But one group of early browsers in the first forests, the chevrotains, evolved a more complex and efficient digestive apparatus. There are two species, one smaller than the other in the South-east Asian forests. There is a third, the water chevrotain in West Africa, and a fourth in India. Such a wide distribution is a strong indication of the chevrotains' antiquity, suggesting that they appeared at a time when tropical forests were more continuous than they are today.

Chevrotains stand about a foot high and have pencil-thin legs, large lustrous eyes and small ears. Like the forest rhino and tapirs, they are largely solitary creatures though the males when they encounter one another may fight. Although they are sometimes called mouse-deer, they do not have antlers. Their only offensive weapons are two teeth, one on either side of the upper jaw, that are enlarged into short tusks. Being so small, and feebly armed, they are an easy meal for leopards or pythons, so unlike tapirs and the hairy rhinos, they do not amble

Brazilian tapir South America ▷
Malayan tapir and calf ▷

nonchalantly through the forest browsing in an unhurried confident way. Instead, they feed quickly, collecting fallen fruit and leaves from low bushes and swallowing them immediately. They then retire to a secluded hiding place and deploy the technique that, it seems, they were the first to pioneer. They ruminate.

Small lumps of their hastily gathered meals are retrieved from a front compartment of their stomach where they had been stored and brought back up the throat, one at a time, to be given a second more intensive chewing with the back molars. That done, the chevrotain swallows the lump again. This time it continues past the first chamber of the stomach and into a second where it is fermented in a bacterial broth. It is a technique that today is used by many species of leaf-eating mammals.

The broad-leaved forests first developed in places where there was an abundance of rain and still today most require plenty of water at least during some part

94

△ *Hairy rhinoceros, Sumatra*

of the year if they are to maintain their hold. Around thirty million years ago they were more widespread than they are now. But then there was a steady cooling of the climate. Patterns of rainfall changed and wide expanses of the land became less well-watered. This gave the chance for a relatively new kind of plant to come into its own – grass. Slowly a green carpet spread across these ill-watered lands and some mammals ventured out of the forests in order to graze upon it.

Many rodents that had gnawed seeds and roots and leaf buds in the forest, moved out on to the plains and became grass-eaters. Rabbits ventured out as well. They were once classified as rodents but they differ in several important respects, one being that alongside the two large chisel-shaped teeth at the front of the mouth that are a rodent characteristic, they have two smaller teeth, one on each side of the large pair. That is enough to award them a group to themselves and to call them lagomorphs. However, it seems that whether the

Chevrotain, South-east Asia △

relationship between the two groups is close or remote, rodents and lagomorphs share the same none-too-distant ancestors.

Rabbits have their own particular way of digesting leaves. They eat their own droppings. As they doze in their burrows at night, they excrete black sticky pellets, but as soon as these emerge from the anus, the rabbit turns round, takes them into its mouth and swallows them. Back in its stomach the pellets are given a second digestive processing. What is left after this is then voided a few hours later when the rabbits are feeding outside their burrows, as the round dry pellets that you see littering the ground in a rabbit warren.

But it was not only leaf-eaters that ventured out of the forests on to the newly established grasslands. Hunting mammals – cats and dogs, both big and small – followed them. Hawks and eagles flew out from their nests in forest trees to patrol the skies above. Out on the open plains, there were far fewer places for leaf-eaters to shelter than there had been in the forest.

Rabbits, voles and ground squirrels were able to create hiding places for

△ *Columbian ground squirrel, Canada*   *Viscachas, Argentina* ▷

themselves. They excavated burrows and flourished in vast numbers. Prairie dogs – which, in spite of their name are not dogs but sizeable ground squirrels form immense towns. One such in Texas, years ago, was said to cover 64,000 square kilometres and contain 400 million inhabitants. The biggest of these plains-living rodents is the South American viscacha, a cousin of the forest-living nut-burying agouti. It looks like an immense guinea pig, over two feet long, with a broad black band that runs across its nose from cheek to cheek like a grotesque moustache. The tunnels it excavates are so big that you can stand in the entrance of one up to your waist. They live in large colonies, underground cities with dozens of entrances and hundreds of yards of interconnecting passages. On the surface of the ground, in the centre of these huge warrens, there are usually several untidy heaps of stones. These were lugged to the surface by the viscachas during their burrowing operations and laboriously dragged into piles. Why is not certain. The viscachas, however, are certainly

compulsive collectors. If you lose something when out riding in viscacha country, the place to look for it is in the piles on the top of the nearest *viscacheria*.

Some leaf-eaters that moved out on to the plains, however, were altogether
too big to find safety in holes. They had to protect themselves in a different
way. Some did so by becoming even bigger. The small forest rhinoceroses
grew into two-ton monsters with skins so tough that even the claws of a lion or
a tiger can make little impression on them. In India, the one-horned rhino developed a skin so thick it is pleated into joints to allow the body within a little
movement. On the African savannahs, two different kinds of rhinos evolved,
the black and the so-called white. In fact the two species are very similar in colour but the white owes its name to a misunderstanding of the Afrikaans name
'weit'. This refers to the animals 'wide' upper lip, which is very different from
that of the slightly smaller black rhino, whose upper lip is prolonged into a mobile point. Well able to take care of themselves and with a need to wander
widely in search of the great quantities of grass they must have to sustain their
immense bulk, adult rhinos are largely solitary animals. They are also extremely
intolerant of company and not only readily charge an approaching human being but one another. Almost a third of female black rhinos and a half of the
males die from wounds.

Another giant has taken to the rivers. The hippopotamus is not perhaps immediately thought of as an eater of grass, since its spends all its days in water,
but in fact it lives on little else. At night, it clambers out of the river, usually
along well-defined and long-established paths and comes up to feed on the
plain. Smooth green lawns beside a gently flowing river may look idyllic camp
sites, but in Africa it may be very ill-advised to pitch a tent on them if a quick
inspection reveals a muddy well-trodden gap in the river bank and large droppings on the grass.

The hippos do not use their teeth like conventional grazers. Instead they nip
the grass with their huge leathery lips, ripping up the leaves with sways of the
head. They may walk for a couple of miles away from the river and enterprising individuals may even spend a day in a distant mud wallow so that they can
feed on pastures even farther away the following night. Most however, return
to the river by daybreak.

Life in the water has brought considerable changes to the hippo body. Their
eyes, ears and nostrils are placed high on the head so that they can see, hear and
smell what is going on above the surface while remaining totally submerged
except for the very top of their heads. They do not have any sweat glands to

◁ *Black rhinoceros, Kenya*   *Swimming hippopotamus, Kenya* ▷ ▷

help cool their bodies. The river water does that for them. They have also lost virtually all their hair. Hair does not function as an insulator in water and in any case a hippo is in little danger of getting seriously chilled there or even out on land at night. The absence of hair risks a back getting sunburnt during the day. The hippo's skin, however, is protected in a different way – with a kind of sun cream. Numerous glands in its skin produce a mucus that turns a reddish brown on exposure to air. Even so, their naked skin is very permeable and loses liquid so easily and quickly that a hippo out of water in the sunshine rapidly becomes seriously dehydrated. As a consequence almost the only time a hippo will venture out of water during the day is when it is raining.

The hippo's front teeth, no longer used for collecting grass, have become adapted instead for display and for fighting. The males threaten one another by yawning, opening their mouths to an alarming degree and showing off the great yellowing tusks on either side of their jaws. If such threats are not enough to settle an argument, rival males will fight, stabbing at one another with their front incisors which may become badly chipped in the process.

Why hippos should have taken to this amphibious existence can only be a guess. It can hardly have been to escape enemies, for lions, the only land predators that animals of their size need fear, are more active at night than they are during the day. In any case, rivers harbour predators and crocodiles can and do attack young hippo calves.

Perhaps it was the easy life that enticed hippos into the river. Lazing around in tepid water does not demand a great expenditure of energy. The water, after all, supports the huge body and only slight movements are needed to move from one place to another if there should be any need to do so – which there is not for most of the time. With such few demands on one's energy, there is no need for huge meals and indeed a hippo has a surprisingly small appetite for an animal that may weigh up to three tons.

Size is, in itself, an advantage to a grass eater. The longer a leaf-eater can keep a meal in its stomach the better chance it has of digesting it properly. The longer it is kept, the bigger the storage vat required and the bigger the frame that is needed to carry such a large container. So there is a tendency among vegetarians to grow large.

The elephant has taken this trend to extremes and has a particular need to, for its food consists not only of leaves but on occasion coarse woody twigs that require a very long time indeed to be processed. Its ancestors, some believe, came not from the forests but from the rivers. They were somewhat pig-like in shape and the size of a small hippopotamus. When they emerged and started to graze on the plains they became very big indeed. Their stomachs are so large they can retain their meals for a very long time. Our own food takes about twenty-four hours to pass through our bodies. An elephant's takes two and a half days.

North America developed its own particular group of grazers. One was a creature about the size of a hare. It had four toes on its fore legs but only two on its back. Its descendants grew steadily bigger, diversified with several different species and eventually spread both westwards across the land bridge to Asia and also southwards along the Panamanian land link that led to South America. They all had long necks, relatively small heads, a cleft upper lip and only two toes on their front legs as well as their hind. Eventually, around ten thousand years ago, the North American species became extinct, but their descendants elsewhere still flourish.

The Asiatic branch of the family are the camels. They have become adapted to living in desert conditions. They can close their nostrils to keep out sand during sandstorms. They will eat the driest thorniest vegetation that no other animal will touch and they can store food as fat in the humps on their backs that sustain them during long periods of famine. They have also modified the physiological workings of their bodies so that they can exist on a minimum of water. Their droppings are extremely dry and their urine very concentrated. They can allow the temperatures of their bodies to rise to heights that few other mammals can tolerate and so do not have to expend precious liquid on sweat until cooling in that way becomes absolutely necessary. As a consequence of all these adaptations, they can live for two months without drinking. When at last they do reach water, they are able to take up thirty gallons at a single sitting.

Such stalwart creatures can survive in the harshest deserts and human beings when they encountered them were quick to domesticate them. Using them as carriers of food and water, people were able to make journeys across deserts that none could have made unaided. This domestication took place around four thousand years ago, so long ago in fact that it was assumed that no wild Asiatic camels still existed. In 1878, however, a Russian explorer, Przewalski discovered some camels in the deserts of Lop-nur in what is now far western China, north of Tibet. They were smaller than domesticated camels, a rather paler brown in colour with two relatively small conical humps on their backs. He believed that they were truly wild animals. Their descendants still survive and genetic studies have now confirmed that these are indeed wild stock.

Another species of camel, known as the dromedary, lives in Arabia. This has

Wild Asiatic camels, Mongolia ▷▷

only one hump and has become specifically adapted to the baking heat of these more southerly deserts. It too was domesticated at a very early date, put by some specialists as being six thousand years ago, but no wild stock can now be found.

The South American descendants of those ancestral North American camels also were domesticated at a very early date. They have become the traditional beasts of burden in the Andes – llamas and the longer-haired alpacas. But neither of these creatures exist in the wild. Both are thought to be the result of many centuries for domesticated breeding, though exactly what their lineage may be is disputed. There are however two wild forms that still survive, the guanaco which is brown with white underparts and the vicuna which is smaller, paler in colour and particularly graceful.

The plains of North America, fifty million years ago, were also grazed by another small herbivore. A distant relation of the ancestral rhinos, it walked, like them, on three toes. It found safety from the carnivores of the time – huge wolf-like dogs and sabre-toothed cats – in speed. The longer your legs in proportion to your body, the bigger your stride and the faster you can run. This animal's central toe became elongated and its nail thickened into a hoof. The other two toes on either side became shorter. It was the ancestral horse.

Horses first appeared in North America. As the grasslands spread, so these animals colonised them and evolved into bigger and more varied forms. During this time, a land bridge existed between North America and Asia across what is now the Bering Strait. The increasingly successful horses crossed it and spread across Asia and into Europe. Prehistoric man twenty-five thousand years ago hunted them and drew pictures of them on the walls of caves. They are believed to be the ancestors of all domesticated horses. Great herds of them survived into recent times. The Russian explorer, Przewalski, who discovered the wild camels, also found small herds of wild horses in central Asia and the species was given his name. But by this time, they had been hunted so intensively that few were left. By the beginning of the twentieth century, all wild specimens seemed to have disappeared totally. But some survived in zoos and their offspring are now being released in their former lands in the hope of preventing the species from disappearing altogether.

But other species of horses continued the family's spread from Europe down into the Middle East and into Africa. Donkeys managed to find enough to eat in dry stony country, and zebras flourished on the more fertile open savannahs of Africa. Why zebras should have developed stripes is something of a mystery. The old suggestion that the conspicuous black and white patterns help to break up the

animal's profile and so assist in making it less conspicuous is no longer thought to be true. Anyone travelling in Africa who gazes at a herd of zebra on the horizon will find it hard to believe that the theory can ever have been thought credible. Even half a mile away the animals are very conspicuous indeed and certainly much more so than the sandy, tawny coloured lions that may be crouched invisibly in the thicker grass, stalking them. Nor, when you see a lion breaking cover and leaping on to a galloping zebra's haunches, can you believe that the stripes in any way dazzle the hunter. Another suggestion has been made that the alternate bands of black and white absorb heat in a different way and so create faint currents in the air that help to keep the animal cool. One function, however, has been demonstrated. The stripes, which vary significantly from one animal to another, certainly serve to identify an individual to other members in its group.

Zebras and horses have their own solution to the problem of digesting grass. They do not retain their meals in their stomachs for great lengths of time like rhinos, nor do they eat their droppings like rabbits. Instead, they have developed an extremely long addition to their hind-gut, called the caecum, which

Przewalski's horse, relocated in △
the Cévennes, France

significantly increases the length of time taken for their food to pass through their bodies.

The most successful of all the large grass-eaters, however, belong to a different group altogether. They are cousins of the forest-living chevrotains. The evidence of this relationship can be seen in their toes. Chevrotains have only two functioning toes on each foot, though the African species has two much reduced digits on either side of each leg that do not touch the ground. Their plains-living descendants are similarly two toed. These are the cloven-hoofed grass-eaters – deer and cattle, antelopes and gazelles. And they too, like the chevrotains, ruminate in order to digest their meals of leaves.

The lengthening of legs and the reduction in the numbers of toes brought the same benefit to these cloven-hoofed animals as it did to the horses. It enabled them to run at speed, an invaluable talent on the open plains. They also adopted the other safety measure of living in herds. An animal by itself on the African savannahs, is an obvious target for a stalking lion. It has only its own eyes and ears to detect approaching danger. If, however, it feeds in the company of a dozen or more others, there will always be one animal with its head raised and its ears cocked ready to spot a lion before it gets close enough to launch an attack. And if and when that lion does charge, there are so many fleeing bodies that the chances of one particular animal being picked out as prey are much smaller than if the animal was by itself.

Living in big groups, however, complicates an animal's social life. A zebra stallion has to compete with other males if he is to father foals. And a zebra mare may see many alternative males in the herd from whom she might select a mate. She is only sexually receptive for a short period each year. As that time approaches a plains zebra stallion does his best to gather as many mares as possible around him so that he can keep his eye on them – or to be more precise, his nose, for he can tell by the smell of their urine when that important moment is about to arrive. While waiting, he has to chase away any other young stallion who might have similar ambitions. He issues fair warning to young hopefuls approaching his group of mares by wrinkling his lip and exposing his formidable teeth. If an intruding male persists, then there will be a fight. The two circle trying to bite each other's legs. If neither is intimidated, they start to slam one another with their necks. They try to bite and kick. Flanks may be gashed and ears torn. Eventually one – usually the intruder – will back off and gallop away, leaving the victor to claim his prize.

Gazelles have similar mating problems but their battles have become more

◁ *Zebra males fighting, Kenya*

ritualised, more influenced by appearance and gesture and less determined by physical violence. Horns can certainly be used as weapons, but their size and shape are also a good guide to an individual's health and strength. Contests between gazelles, therefore, can be settled economically, without the gross expenditure of any energy and no risk of injury.

A male impala guarding a group of females displays his weaponry by parading up and down with his head erect, his ears held back and his tail clamped firmly down. The mere sight of his gracefully curving horns may well be enough to convince rivals of his superior strength. If, however, another male decides to contest this, he will give notice by raising his tail, showing its pale underside, yawning and flicking his tongue. He then lowers his head inviting battle. The rivals will then go through all the movements of a fight, facing one another head-on, advancing and retreating – but without actually touching one another. Once again, there is an opportunity for one or the other to back down. If both persist, then a third round of the contest begins. Now the two do actually meet and lock horns. Back and forth they push one another. They separate and re-engage, and stab at one another's necks. But blood is seldom shed. One

△ *Zebra male threatening, Kenya*

contestant eventually retreats leaving the victor stalking stiffly around, flaunting his horns with head held high.

It is not only a male's rivals who assess the quality of his horns. So do the females. They, after all, also have a choice in these matters and there is increasing evidence that a female impala will choose to graze beside the male that has the most symmetrical and well-developed regalia on his head.

Females of different kinds of antelope developed different predilections. Each species has horns of a shape that is as characteristic of its kind as is the different coloured plumage of a bird. So horns – straight as rapiers, backwardly curved like scimitars, ridged by spirals or with tips tilted vertically upwards – proclaim not only health and strength, but specific identity.

Horns are bony outgrowths of the skull that are capped with keratin, the same material that forms hooves and our own finger nails. Once they have developed, a male antelope retains them for the rest of his life. But inevitably, as they increase in size with age, they become a heavier burden.

The other great group of cloven-hoofed grass-eaters, the deer, manage to avoid such permanent loads – at least to some extent. They only flaunt the

111

Impala males fighting, Kenya △

badges of fitness on their heads for part of the year. During the winter, a red deer stag is without any encumbering headgear as he searches the meagre vegetation for food. This is no time to be carrying unnecessary strength-sapping weight. But as spring comes and summer follows, so the stags become better fed and have energy to spare. A pair of bumps appears on their forehead. These grow rapidly upwards, nourished by blood vessels in the skin that covers them. The pillars begin to branch. The older and bigger the individual, the more branches his antlers will develop. Swift though growth is, it nonetheless takes four to five months before antlers are fully developed. Then the skin that covers them begins to split and shrivel until it hangs in tatters from the new white bone of the antlers, often staining them red with blood. The newly crowned males then clean their antlers by knocking them against trees or thrashing them on the ground, preparing them for display and, if necessary, battle.

The contests between male deer are just as ritualised as those between antelopes and the size of antlers is just as influential in the eyes of both males and females. But then, after the jousts of autumn, their function is over for the year. They weaken around their base and drop off. In American species, this happens in early winter, but in Europe deer may well keep their antlers throughout the winter and beyond, so that within a few weeks of shedding them in spring, they start growing them again.

So eating grass can lead, indirectly, to great social complexities. It can also, in some instances, compel animals to make journeys that are fraught with danger. Many kinds of grass are markedly poor in minerals and grazers must necessarily make good such deficiencies. Mountain goats in Montana climb up sheer cliffs to reach salt licks. In the Upper Amazon, brocket deer wade bravely into quicksands, all the time pumping their fore legs to keep themselves above the surface, in order to reach mineral rich water welling up from the depths. And in Africa, buffalo climb up the slopes of Mount Kenya to altitudes of over nine thousand feet in order to dig out particularly salty iron-rich clay with their horns.

But perhaps the most impressive example of the lengths to which grass-eaters will go to obtain minerals is shown by the elephants of Mount Elgon in Kenya. In one place, on the flanks of this immense extinct volcano there are volcanic deposits that contain abundant salts. Elephants for centuries have visited a cave here. They boldly walk into its depths, along a passage so long and winding that no natural light reaches far into it. In any case, the

◁ *Red deer roaring in rut, Great Britain*

elephants usually visit the cave at night so that even a few yards beyond its mouth the blackness is total.

We installed tiny infra-red lights that to the unaided eye look no brighter than a glowing cigarette end, and watched the animals on specially sensitive electronic cameras. They move through the blackness with the greatest caution. They test each footstep, feeling carefully for a foothold, stepping over huge boulders the position of which they seem to remember from past visits. Eventually they reach the rock face at the far end. Here they use their tusks to gouge out the coarse sandy rock and then pick up lumps of it from the ground at their feet with their trunks and crunch it with their huge molars. Elephant calves usually stay close to their mothers and so they too walk deep into the caves. They do not seem to have acquired the taste for salt and soon become bored in the pitch darkness. You can watch them fumbling around, playing with boulders that they can only feel but cannot see. But it is important that they make the journey, so that they will learn the route into the cave and be able to maintain the tradition. Judging from the depth of the cave, the Mount Elgon elephants must have been collecting minerals from this site for centuries. Indeed, it may well be that these huge caves were actually created by the elephants themselves as, generation after

△ *Elephants tusking for salt in the caves of*
Mount Elgon, Kenya

generation, they dug deeper and deeper into the cliff, following the seam that was particularly rich in the minerals they need so badly.

The need for particular minerals is also the fundamental cause of one of the most spectacular of all animal movements, the annual migration of the wildebeest in east Africa. The herds spend the wet season down on the plains of the south-eastern Serengeti in Tanzania. The soils here are volcanic and rich in minerals, but towards the end of May, the rains begin to fail. The grass begins to wither and water holes to dry. The wildebeest herds now start to move away, plodding or gently cantering one behind the other in long columns. They travel north and cross the Mara River into the Masai Mara plains of southern Kenya. Here patchy showers of rain have produced areas of tall grass and there is water to drink from the rivers. But then some time towards the end of the year, just as the rains begin again, the wildebeest start to leave. In vast jostling numbers they surge back across the Mara river. Giant crocodiles, lying in wait for them, take hundreds, but tens of thousands complete the crossing. Why should they leave, when the grass is springing once more on the plains of the Mara? It is because these pastures are severely deficient in phosphorus. That precious and essential mineral they can only find in the newly sprouting

Wildebeest attacked by a crocodile, Tanzania △
Wildebeest crossing the Mara river, Kenya ▷▷

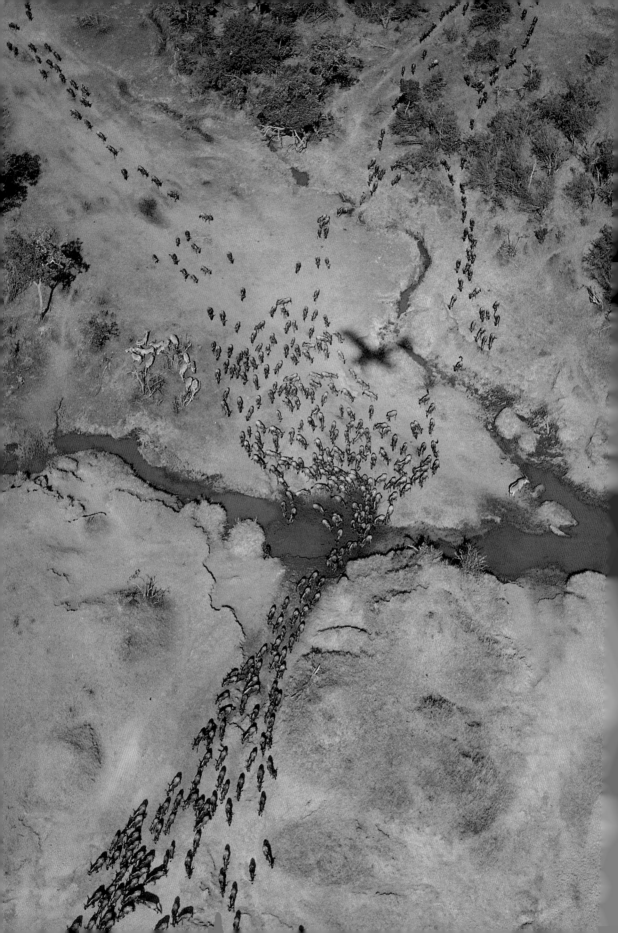

grass of the Serengeti that they were forced to leave when it started to wither six months earlier.

Dietary inadequacies, coupled with seasonal changes in the weather also cause major problems to caribou. During the summer, the caribou of north-western Canada and Alaska, not far from the continent's northern coast, feed on a wide variety of broad-leaved plants including cotton grass and low dwarf willow. Here the females give birth. But when the weather gets even colder with the coming of the autumn, many of these plants shed their leaves. Even those that keep their leaves become buried beneath snow. The caribou can no longer stay out on the open tundra and they start on a long journey southwards to areas where patches of coniferous forest offer some shelter from the biting winds and blizzards. The journey is several hundred miles long and may take weeks. The animals move slowly, around two miles an hour, and often in single file feeding when they can and travelling both day and night. How far they move in twenty-four hours varies according to snow conditions. Sometimes it may be as much as thirty miles, sometimes only a tenth of that distance. They follow regular pathways, but blizzards and deep snow drifts may

◁ *Wildebeest on migration, Tanzania*

Migrating caribou, Alaska △
Caribou crossing a lake, Canada ▷▷

here and there compel them to vary their route. But at length, they reach their winter feeding grounds.

Here they will stay for several months. The food, however, is poor, consisting largely of a kind of lichen, known inaccurately as reindeer 'moss', that grows over the rocks. To reach it, the caribou may have to sweep aside snow, which they do with their antlers. These have a branch close to their base which projects forward and serves as a shovel. For this reason, females as well as males develop antlers, unlike any other member of the deer family. But the lichen on which they feed, like the grasses of the Masai Mara, are poor in certain minerals. These are essential for the females if they are to produce milk for their young, so even before the warming spring sun has melted the ground, the herd starts to travel north again. The round trip is about a thousand miles long.

With all these stratagems, techniques and physical adaptations, some mammals have managed to become very effective grazers. But grass has also evolved ways to defend itself against the millions of cropping muzzles that attack it daily. Many arm their leaves with tiny blades of silica projecting from their margins. A careless slide of your finger down the leaf of some species can cut your skin and convince you very quickly of their presence. This silica makes the grass so gritty that it wears down the teeth of any animal that chews it. Over millennia, grass-eaters have responded to this. Horses evolved very long teeth, and very deep jaw-bones to accommodate them, and they move upwards as their surfaces are worn down. Elephants have massive grinders that are a foot long. There are two on each side of the jaws of an adult. As they wear, so two more form at the back of the jaws which gradually move forward displacing the old worn down teeth which are then shed. Each is larger than its predecessor, thus compensating for the elephant's increase in size as it ages. But each jaw on each side can only produce six molars. When the last set has arrived and been worn down the aged animal can no longer feed properly and will be close to the end of its life.

Plants and mammals seem to have kept pace with one another on this score, but grasses developed yet another device to maintain their hold on their territory. They grew long horizontal stems lying so close to the ground that they cannot normally be reached by muzzles and nipping teeth. It is from these that new leaves sprout and these leaves grow, not along the length of the blade as others do but from their very base close to the rhizome. So when grass leaves are cropped they can re-grow immediately.

Today there seems to be a truce between grasses and those that eat them. The

organisms that are most likely to displace grasses from their lands are not animals but other plants. If through some change in environmental conditions, a
plain covered in grass becomes better-watered, seeds blown or transported
from a nearby forest may germinate and get a root-hold. If a bush begins to
grow, its roots are likely to collect water needed by the grass. Worse, its spreading branches will cut out the light on which the grass depends. So the grass has
to retreat and a bare patch develops on the earth beneath the bush. If that happens over a wide area, the forest could return. But deer and wildebeest, antelopes and rabbits will nip off the shoots of such seeds. Elephants are likely to
pull up young bushes. They may even knock down full-grown trees growing
on the edges of the forest and open up new territory for grasses.

So grasses have not only achieved a truce with those animals that feed on
them. They have now formed an alliance with the grazers that ensures their hold
on the pampas of South America, the plains of Europe, the prairies of the American west and the savannahs of Africa – a sizeable proportion of all the fertile land
on earth. And on these vast open expanses graze immense herds that constitute
the greatest concentration of meat and muscle to be found anywhere on earth.

123

Elephants feeding on trees, Kenya △

5

MEAT EATERS

Meat is muscle. It is one of the richest, the most energy-packed, of all foods. So it is hardly surprising that when leaf-eating mammals established themselves in the forests and grasslands of the world, other mammals appeared which hunted the leaf-eaters for the sake of their flesh.

Hunters need weapons. Butchers need tools. These meat-eaters evolved teeth that served both these functions – two pairs of long canines, like daggers, one on each side of their jaws with which to stab their victims and two sets of jagged blades called carnassials, farther back in the jaw, which slice against one another like the blades of secateurs, with which to cut up the carcass. These are the hall-marks of a carnivore. Today, wherever in the world there are substantial numbers of mammals browsing on leaves or on grass, there will be others lurking nearby armed with such weapons, waiting to attack.

The European stoat is not a large animal, only about a foot long from the tip of its nose to the end of its slim, sinuous, softly-furred body. It is brown above and cream beneath, with a short four-inch-long black-tipped tail. It weighs only about a tenth as much as a rabbit. Yet it hunts them. Crouching in the long grass, it creeps close to an unsuspecting victim sitting not far from its burrow. Once within range, the stoat deliberately shows itself. It starts to dance, leaping up and down apparently chasing its own tail. It somersaults. It bounces up again and makes a back flip. It disappears momentarily into the long grass and then swoops up again. The rabbit, maybe only a couple of yards or so away, is transfixed. It stops nibbling and stares with bulging eyes at this extraordinary performance. Suddenly the stoat bursts out from the grass, stabs its teeth into the back of the rabbit's neck smashing the rear end of its skull. The rabbit's legs twitch for a few moments. Then it slumps motionless. It is dead and the stoat begins the laborious business of hauling the great slack body back to its burrow.

Stoats are so active and burn up so much energy so swiftly that they need to feed every few hours. In spring a female must hunt with particular zeal for then she is likely to have young in her den and she has not only to feed herself but to maintain a regular supply of milk for them. Her brood is large – as many as a dozen young kits. They are born blind and naked. The male who is their father plays no part whatever in caring for them. She must look after them by herself, first supplying them with milk and then with fragments of meat. So she has to hunt almost continuously and much of the time she is compelled to leave her young unguarded.

In her absence from the den a male stoat may pay a visit. He is unlikely to be her mate. Most probably he is a young male, perhaps only a year or so old. Inside the den he finds the naked youngsters. Even at three weeks old, they are still blind so they cannot see him, but they instinctively recognise his nature, perhaps from his scent, for the infant females among them react to him by making high-pitched trilling calls and lifting their hind quarters. One after the other, the male copulates with them – and then scampers away.

The eggs he has fertilised within the kits do not develop immediately. For

△ *Stoat with newly killed rabbit, England*

the time being the young use all the food brought to the den by their mother to build their own bodies. It will be several months before they are fully grown and are able to get sufficient food to spare for investment in their offspring. But as soon as that moment comes, they will do so without any delay caused by seeking a mate. Stoats do not live long – two or three years only – so it is important for them to get on with the business of their lives as swiftly as they can. Neither the young females, nor indeed the male could have seized their reproductive opportunities any earlier than this.

The stoat and its still smaller European cousin, the weasel, belong to a group called the mustelids. Some of their relations – badgers and skunks – will readily vary their diet with earthworms and snails, fruit, seeds and even leaves. But others including polecats, martens and the wolverine, the Arctic giant of the family which grows to nearly four feet long, are predominantly eaters of meat.

One of the first to take to this diet – and develop the teeth needed to do so – lived some thirty-five million years ago in the forests of North America. An early descendant, very little changed, is still found in the south-western corner of the continent. At first sight it looks very like the familiar European red fox though its body is a little smaller and rather more elongated and its coat is grey rather than reddish-brown. But the behaviour of this grey fox, as it is known, is hardly fox-like. It spends much of its time on the ground but when it is alarmed it is quite likely to run straight up a tree trunk. It achieves this unexpected feat by twisting its forelegs inwards to grasp the trunk and pushing itself upwards with its hind legs which have particularly long claws. Once it reaches the branches, it leaps with great confidence from one to the other, using its long shaggy tail as a counter-balance. It is sufficiently agile in the tree tops to be able to catch squirrels and birds. It even ambushes rats and mice, hares and rabbits by crouching on a branch and leaping down on top of them. But it also takes insects, and a wide range of fruit such as wild cherries, grapes and berries. It was from a creature very like this that all the dogs of today are descended.

As dogs spread through the Americas, their bodies became adapted to suit the land they colonised. One of the least known of them is the bush dog. It lives in rain forests from Guyana to Brazil. Its legs are short, its body squat so that it looks like a somewhat portly version of the domestic dachshund. That suits it well for running through the undergrowth. It also has webbed feet and spends much of its time around rivers, looking for turtles and fish. From the few first-hand observations that have been made of these rare creatures in the wild, it seems that they live in packs and are extremely sociable. They trot in

◁ *Long-tailed weasel with a mouse, North America*

single file along well-worn paths through the forest and do so in a particular and habitual order. The females are at the front with the most senior of them in the lead, and the males follow behind. They mark their territories with scent, lavishly spreading urine over particular signposts and indeed themselves. When they re-tire to their den at night, they pile on top of one another in what are called 'sleep heaps'. This sociability is a characteristic that manifests itself again and again in the dog family.

Other kinds of dog spread northwards through the temperate woodlands and into the tundra. Here it is vital for any mammal to conserve its body heat as effi-ciently as possible. So the fox that lives in the Arctic has a tail, ears, and legs that are short and stubby. Its fur is particularly thick and fine and grows right over its paws. Thanks to these adaptations, it can endure temperatures of 70° below zero. Some Arctic foxes are dark bluish grey in summer and pale slightly when winter comes. Others turn pure white and are so perfectly camouflaged that they are able to creep unnoticed to within pouncing distance of their prey.

But prey of any kind in the Arctic is seldom found easily. In winter, these foxes travel far out across the sea ice, hundreds of miles from the coast. Here they

△ *Bush dog with young, South America,*

may be able to scavenge on the remains of seals caught by polar bears. Inland their diet is largely lemmings. But when spring comes, for a short period, there is a glut of food. Lemmings suddenly increase in numbers. Ground nesting birds such as snow geese fly up from the south to nest on the tundra. Seabirds – guillemots, kittiwakes and auklets – arrive from all over the Arctic and prepare to nest on the cliffs. The foxes' trails, as they clamber up the cliffs in search of eggs and nestlings, are easy to trace. Those parts of the cliff that are very difficult for the foxes to reach, where the birds are safer and nest more successfully, are soon covered in white droppings. In contrast, the grassy ledges which the foxes use frequently as corridors to reach various parts of the cliff, are soon cleared of nesting birds. In consequence the foxes' paths show up like a special class of road on a map, picked out in green.

The foxes collect far more food at this time of the year than they can possibly consume. But that does not stop them from hunting. They continue to do so intensively throughout the weeks of spring and then dig holes and bury those bodies that they cannot eat. In these low temperatures, their kills will remain edible for months.

Arctic fox, Canada △

Neither the Arctic foxes' prey nor the rabbits caught by the stoat are able to defend themselves very effectively. But some carnivores tackle prey that is powerful enough to kill them. The bison is the biggest animal in North America. A bull can weigh nearly a ton. It is immensely strong. A blow from its huge horns could crack a skull. A kick from its legs could break a spine. But in winter, hunger drives wolves in the northern part of the continent to attack bison.

The grey wolf that lives here is the biggest of all dogs. Such great size is what you might expect, since a big animal retains its heat more successfully than a small one. It stands over three feet tall at the shoulder and is over six feet long from its nose to the end of its tail. It is almost twice as big as an Alsatian. But even so, there is no way in which a single dog even of this size could bring down an adult bison. Grey wolves can only do so by working as a team.

The scrubland and open prairie where the bison graze has little cover. If the wolves get close to a group of them, the bison gather together, facing outwards, with their small vulnerable calves at the centre. But they cannot stay in such a formation forever. They have to disperse to feed. If the wolves find one somewhat away from the main herd, they might alarm it sufficiently to make it run to join the rest. If others look up from their grazing, they too may gallop away. Then the wolves will have a chance,

The pack gives chase. There may be twenty or thirty of them. The pursuit may last off and on for days during which the herd, followed by the pack, will travel many miles. The wolves are testing the bison, trying to identify one that may be less strong because of age or sickness. It is likely to be one of those lagging behind. Gradually the pack focus their attention on a particular individual and run in a group behind it, snapping at its heels.

Their claws are not sharp enough to give them a hold on the bison's flanks. All they can do is to try and get a grip with their teeth. These are their only weapons. If one does succeed, it may slow the bison sufficiently for others to get a hold as well. The bison may manage to shake them off, but the wolves are persistent. It may be half an hour before their victim in weakened enough for them to surround it. Now, with wolves threatening it face-on, others can get a hold on its underbelly. Eventually they bring it down. They rip at its stomach, disembowelling it. But there is no way that they can kill a bison quickly. So they feed on it, tearing at its flesh, ripping out its entrails while it is still alive. There will be enough food on a single bison to last the wolf pack, if necessary, for a week.

Teamwork like this demands discipline, and discipline for a wolf, starts

◁ *Grey wolf howling, North America*

early. The young are born in a den selected by their mother. It may be a naturally occurring hole, beneath tree roots or under a boulder, or she may have dug it herself with her strong blunt claws. There may be half a dozen or so pups. They are born blind and do not open their eyes until they are around two weeks old. Their mother licks them regularly. This is not only to keep them clean. The caress of her tongue is also an instruction to them to defecate. Having felt it, the little pup rolls over on to its back and duly obeys. The action, one of the pup's first behavioural responses, is something that it will perform throughout its life as an indication of submission. In the weeks to come the growing pup will use it when

132

△ *Grey wolf defending its kill,*
    North America

Grey wolf with her young, North America ▷

it gets involved in a fight with another and decides that it has had enough of being chivvied and nipped. And as soon as it rolls on to its back, exposing its vulnerable belly, its rival withdraws. In this way, a ranking is established within the new generation.

The pups have huge appetites. Half a dozen take a lot of feeding. When adults return from a successful hunt with full bellies, the pups beg, whining and wagging their tails and licking the corners of an adult's mouth until eventually it disgorges gobbets of meat from its stomach. The cubs may be so persistent that they will keep pestering an adult until it has nothing further to give and then it lets the pups know with a growl.

When the pups are big enough to leave the den, usually between three and ten weeks, the whole pack can once more range widely in search of food. Communication by gesture and by sound is constant. A high tail indicates confidence and, in an argument, aggression. Ears pulled back, the tail held between the legs and a half-crouched posture demonstrates submission. Tail wagging conveys contentment. Whimpers and squeals indicate anxiety or irritation. And it is by such communications that the pack comes to communal decisions, such as when to set out on a hunt.

This year's youngsters may still not be sufficiently big and strong to take

part. So they, together sometimes with older members of the pack who can now no longer keep up on a long chase, settle down in a resting place, a rendezvous. Here they will remain until the rest of the pack return if the hunt has failed or until they hear the triumphant howls that signal success. And when the pack is reunited, the hunters will surrender some of the spoils from their bellies to those who remained behind.

There is a price to pay, however, for this disciplined social life. The difficulties of hunting are such that the number of pups a pack can raise in a year is limited and usually only the top dogs, the alpha male and his mate, will breed. The junior members are physiologically capable of doing so but aggressive behaviour from their seniors prevents this. Junior bitches in the pack, if they show too much interest in the senior male, will be drive away by his mate and he will react in a similar way towards optimistic young males. Both will interrupt incipient copulation among their juniors. The situation cannot remain unchanged for ever. Eventually old age and failing strength brings changes in the hierarchy. Young vigorous individuals may break away to found their own packs. But it is

△ *Young grey wolf begging for food, North America*   *Fennec fox, North Africa* ▷

very unusual for a pack, particularly where conditions are hard, to rear more than a single litter in a year.

North America, throughout the millions of years during which mammals spread around the world, has intermittently been connected to Asia across the Bering Strait. It was during one of these periods of connection that horses first crossed into Asia. Members of the dog family did much the same thing. From Asia they spread into Europe and eventually down through the Middle East to Africa. And as they colonised new territories in the Old World, so they also evolved adaptations that suited their new life styles.

Fennec foxes colonised the Sahara. Just as short ears and rounded bodies reduce heat loss for the Arctic fox, so thin bodies and huge ears, only thinly covered with hair increase it. Those are exactly what the fennec has. But even with these cooling adaptations, heat in the open desert at mid-day can become intolerable and at this time the little fennecs shelter in their underground dens. There they pant rapidly, taking almost unbelievably up to 690 breaths a minute but keeping their tongues curled to minimise the loss of precious water from their saliva. Only when the sun has dropped below the horizon and the desert has started to cool, will they venture out.

Other animals also emerge from their shelters at this time in order to feed. Small rodents, gerbils and mouse-like gundis scurry from plant to plant. The fennecs hunt for them in a most un-dog-like way. Most dogs seek prey with their noses. But that technique is ineffective here. Smell requires moisture to transport it and there is little moisture in the baked desert. Instead, the fennec uses its huge ears that serve it so well as cooling radiators in an additional way. With these they can detect the slightest sound, even the faint scratching made by a beetle as it clambers over sand grains. In this hungry land the fennec does not despise a meal of insects. But to survive it needs bigger prey as well. A gerbil will provide it with a mouthful of meat but it also yields something else which the fennecs must have. Moisture. Unlike bigger desert-living animals such as antelope and many birds, the fennec only very rarely makes special journeys to look for water. It manages to extract enough liquid from the bodies of its prey for it never to drink. So it is able to stay permanently on its home patch among the dunes.

South of the Sahara, on the open savannahs of Kenya and Tanzania, conditions are not so extreme and here, there is prey in abundance. The African

△ *Hunting dogs greeting one another, Kenya*

Hunting dogs seeking prey, ▷
chasing wildebeest, ▷
and the kill, East Africa ▷ ▷

hunting dogs, like wolves work together in packs. There are reports of groups containing as many as fifty individuals. A dozen, however, is a more typical number. The animals are about the size of large sheepdogs and are broadly patterned with patches of black and white on a sandy background. Such coloration may well be effective camouflage under some circumstances, but no two individuals are exactly the same, so it also enables members of the pack to recognise one another and at a distance.

Individual packs have particular tastes and traditions in the quarry they select. Some may specialise in hunting zebra, others in tackling ostrich. Most will hunt relatively common creatures such as impala. This antelope can outpace the dogs in a sprint, but the dogs are tireless. Once they have started a chase, they seldom give up. They can maintain a speed of nearly 40 miles an hour over a distance of a couple of miles. Soon they are cantering alongside the impala. If for one reason or another, it runs in a curve, deflected maybe by some obstacle, then some of the dogs at the back of the pack may be able to take a short cut and those that were running at the rear may take over the lead. They have one of the best success rates of any hunters. One pack, in the Ngorongoro Crater, hunted twice a day and caught 85% of the animals it chased.

Only the senior pair in the pack will breed, as is the case with wolves. But hunting dogs have one curious distinction. The long-term core of a wolf pack are the females. Young female wolves stay with their mother and one of them in due course will take over the ruling position. Young males on the other hand tend to emigrate and join other groups. So it is with most group-living mammals. But in the hunting dog pack, it is the males who remain with the group and the females who emigrate. Not only that, but when the females leave, sisters will do so together. The resident males since they are all the offspring of the reigning couple, are themselves brothers. Why this should be so is not clear.

While the ancestors of dogs were evolving in the New World, another different group of carnivores were developing in the forests of the Old. These too were originally tree-dwellers. The animals that most closely resemble them today are the arboreal genets. These are solitary creatures mostly with spotted coats, long tails and bodies so elongated and sinuous that genets seem to flow rather than run as they race soundlessly through the forest branches. Few creatures can travel through trees with such speed, agility and grace. They owe their sure-footedness to a characteristic that the dogs never developed – claws that can be kept sharp by being stropped on bark and which are prevented from blunting by being retracted into sheaths when they are not needed.

Genets are far from specialised in their diet. They will take eggs, insects and fruits. But they are also skilled hunters and are expert at catching birds, squirrels and other rodents. Scent plays an important part in their lives. They anoint the branches through which they romp with both urine and a secretion from a gland beneath their tail. They use these smells to communicate with one another and from them are quick to detect the presence of strangers. Nonetheless, the tree-tops are not the ideal place for communication by smell. Up there, scent disperses quickly. It is more effective down on the ground and down there cousins of the genets, the civets exploit it to the full.

Smells in great variety and varying pungencies seem to dominate the world of the civets. They use it to locate their food – whether it is the surging

Genet, South Africa △

fragrance of distant ripening fruit or the infinitesimal whiff that a small rodent might have left in its footprints. But they too use smell to communicate within the group. The organ that produces these messages – their olfactory larynx as it were – is a large pouch-like gland that lies between their anus and their genitals. This produces an oily substance as thick as honey with a smell that, sampled in strength by the human nose, is so unpleasant as to verge on the nauseating.

However, it has a particular quality that is highly valued by those people who make perfumes for human use. The civet's oil 'exalts' other perfumes. It heightens them, retaining their volatile oils and releasing them so slowly that they linger for a long time. For this reason, humans have greatly valued civet oil for many centuries and have hunted civets entirely for the sake of it. Civets themselves smear their oil on their dunghills and on rocks and branches in their territories as signs of ownership, warning others to keep out. Some merely bend their

△ *African civet*   *Brown hyena tasting scent mark, Zimbabwe* ▷

back legs and drag their rears along the ground. Others will stand on their hands in order to place their pungent posters as high as they can.

One ground living cousin of the civets has brought communication by smell to a particularly high level of complexity. The brown hyena of Africa's Kalahari desert is an obsessive marker of its territory. It lives in clans of a dozen or so. Food is short in the desert and members of the clan have to patrol wide areas in their search for prey or for carrion. Every quarter of a mile or so, they mark. They walk over and straddle a clump of grass, or maybe even a single stem, so that it brushes behind their hind legs. Then, half-crouching, they smear it with oil from their anal gland in much the same way that genets and civets do. But the brown hyena has a special trick.

It produces two kinds of secretion. The first is a white pasty deposit that sticks to the grass stem in a small bead about the size of a match head. Then, as the hyena moves slightly forward, its anal gland contracts further and exudes a smaller black blob from another lobe of its gland which sticks to the grass stem just above the white bead. The two kinds of paste have different properties and broadcast different messages to different audiences. The white bead retains its smell for several weeks. It is a semi-permanent notice that warns off hyenas

belonging to other clans and is a clear and long-lasting statement that this territory is occupied. The black bead's message is shorter-lived. It fades rapidly and disappears entirely after only a few hours. Other members of the clan, passing this way in their search for food will therefore be able to deduce from its relative pungency how long ago it was that one of their number has passed this way and so be able to decide whether the desert is worth a search. There may be as many as 15,000 regularly up-dated signposts in any one clan's territory. All these Old World hunters – genets, civets, hyenas – supplement their meals of meat with vegetables. Some species of civet, indeed, are almost entirely fruit eaters in spite of the fact that they still have teeth that could kill. But one closely related family are dedicated hunters and seldom eat anything but flesh. They are the most specialised of all mammalian hunters. They have short snouts and high-domed skulls, which provide attachments for massive jaw muscles. And they have the sharpest carnassial teeth and the longest canines. These are the cats.

The majority of cat species are solitary hunters living in dense forest. Most have mottled variegated coats that provide them with superlative camouflage. There is usually considerable variation in coat pattern between individuals, so that it is easy to recognise particular animals. Overall colouring also varies greatly. A male tiger caught by an Indian maharajah in the middle of the last century was almost white. He was so intrigued by it, he kept it in his private zoo. There it bred regularly and soon 'white tigers' were distributed among zoos internationally. They are not, however, a separate species. Their coloration is due to a genetic variation known as albinism which occurs in many other species of animal, including mankind. Albino tigers, however, are exceedingly rare in the wild, and one can well understand that such pale and conspicuous animals might find it very difficult indeed to hunt successfully in the darkness of a forest.

Leopards and jaguars show the opposite tendency and often develop a super-abundance of pigment. This is particularly so among the leopards of Malaysia, where almost half the population is virtually black. Particularly dark individuals are popularly known as 'black panthers'. They are, however, true leopards and their spots are often just detectable beneath their jet veil.

Most cats hunt at night. In daylight, their eyesight is as good as ours. At night it is about six times better. They owe this heightened sensitivity to a membrane that many nocturnal mammals belonging to quite different groups have evolved independently. It lies behind the retina of the eye and reflects light that has passed through the retina back on to it. It is a reflection from this layer, the tapetum, that shines back at us if our torches find the eyes of a cat out hunting at night.

Jaguar climbing, South America ▷

Cats from the Old World crossed the Bering land bridge into the New, just as dogs did coming from the other direction. The jaguar spread across both American continents, from the southern deserts of the United States right down to Argentina. The ocelot, a much smaller creature only a little larger than a fox has a similar distribution and has half a dozen cousins each adapted to a particular environment – the tiger cat that lives in the tropical forest, the margay which is particularly at home in trees, the mountain cat found in the high Andes from southern Peru to Chile, Geoffroy's cat that inhabits upland forest, and the pampas cat that hunts on the continent's grasslands.

△ *Jaguar fishing, South America*

Ocelots, South America ▷
Margay cat, Peru ▷

But it is in the Old World, the feline homeland, that cats have their greatest variety. Lynx and wild cats live in the coniferous forest of the north, right down across Europe as far as Spain. In Asia, one of the rarest and the most elusive of all cats, the snow leopard, hunts in the remote and empty valleys of the Himalayas. Half a dozen species – including fishing cats and leopard cats, marbled cats and flat-headed cats – inhabit the rain forests of South-east Asia.

Tigers were once found in most parts of Asia. They were so widespread, living in rain forest, marshlands and dry scrub country, that they developed into separate regional populations sufficiently distinct in size and coat patterns to be classified as sub-species. Many of these, however, are now extinct. Two sub-species, one in Java and one in Bali, have both disappeared and the one that lives in Sumatra and southern China is now extremely rare. The Caspian tiger that once was found from Afghanistan to Turkey has also been exterminated. Even in India, the tiger's range has been greatly reduced. But the biggest sub-species of all still survives – just. It lives far beyond the Arctic Circle in the snows of Siberia. Its size is hardly unexpected since it is advantageous to be big in low temperatures. But the Siberian tiger is spectacularly large. Males, which

◁ *Serval leaping for a bird, South Africa*   *European lynx* △

are bigger than the females, may weigh as much as 700 pounds (306 kilos). The Siberian tiger is the largest of all living terrestrial meat-eaters.

In Africa, there are also specialist cats. The serval, a small species with particularly long legs bounces its way through tall grass pursuing mice and rats. So skilled is it at pouncing and so gymnastic in doing so that it can suddenly switch its attention away from little rodents scurrying ahead of it through the grass and bring down a low-flying bird with a swat of its forepaw. The leopard is almost exclusively a night hunter. In order to get within striking distance of its prey it moves in total silence, placing each front foot with slow tentative movements to make sure that it will not snap a twig or rustle a leaf – and then, with consummate muscular control, it brings its hind foot forward to place it exactly on the space vacated by its forepaw that it has proved to be silent.

The cheetah runs down its prey. Its spine is so flexible that at speed it can bring its long hind legs right forward between its front pair and so make huge bounds. Its claws do not retract completely into their sheaths so that their tips

△ *Indian Tiger*

slightly protrude and thus give its pounding paws the grip of a sprinter's spikes. With these adaptations it can reach a speed of 60 miles an hour, the fastest of all land animals. But it is not a long distance runner. Unless it catches its prey, usually a gazelle, within a minute the cheetah has to give up.

All these cat species, in North and South America, in Asia, Europe and Africa are solitary hunters. There is however one that hunts in a very different way – the lion.

Lions live in prides that can number over twenty. They are seldom seen all together for individual members of the pride may move around the territory independently, joining up for a few days with others or wandering by themselves. Nor does the whole pride hunt at the same time. But they constitute a single social group because they all tolerate one another and seemingly welcome one another's company. The usual explanation for this un-cat-like habit is that lions depend upon team-work for their hunting success.

Lionesses in a pride do indeed often hunt together. They spread out in a line. As they approach a group of grazing wildebeest or zebra, they crouch low in the grass, and stealthily advance towards them. Eventually one of them is

Cheetah hunting, Kenya △

detected. The herd stampedes in a panic. Some almost inevitably run within range of one or other of the lionesses, giving her a good chance to bring it down. But is this intentional teamwork? And if it is, is it so necessary for hunting success as to be the fundamental reason why lionesses live in prides? It is certainly true that a single lion would have very great difficulty in bringing down the biggest of the grazers on the plains – giraffe, eland or buffalo. But then they have no need to tackle such difficult prey. There are great numbers of wildebeest, gazelles and zebra and a lion is fully capable of killing one of these entirely by itself. And statistics compiled over many years by patient observations of a single pride show that hunting in teams might even be disadvantageous for an individual. A lion, hunting by itself, will catch its prey, on average, once in seven attempts. If several hunt together, they will certainly be more successful and kill once in every two or three attempts. But team hunters have to share their kill. So a single lion after seven attempts may get a whole gazelle to itself, whereas if it hunted a similar number of times with ten or so companions and brought down three gazelles, it would only get a third of one. Of course, this is something of an over-simplification. There could be other factors. It might be better to eat a little but frequently than a great deal at longer intervals. And a group of lions is

152

△ *Lion killing zebra, East Africa*

certainly better able to defend a kill from marauders like hyenas than a single one. But there is also another reason, apart from success in hunting, that causes lions to live in prides.

Females in a pride greatly outnumber males. It is they who form its social and permanent core and they who will present a united front and repel any rival groups that may try and invade. All these females are related – sisters or mothers and daughters. They collaborate, often going out hunting in groups of half a dozen or so. They show affection towards one another's cubs and nursing mothers on occasion will allow their nephews and nieces to suckle.

There are seldom more than three or four males in the pride. They may or may not be brothers, but they are in no way related to the females. They are, when it comes to mating with the females, remarkably uncompetitive. One of them will notice that a lioness is coming into oestrus and guard her until that moment of sexual receptivity arrives. Then he will mate with her repeatedly – once every twenty minutes or so – during the few days that her oestrus lasts. As several females in the pride often come into oestrus at much the same time there is little need for the males to compete with one another on this score.

Lioness and cubs, Kenya △

But the males are not permanent members of the pride and seldom stay with it for more than three years. During that period they may be challenged several times by small wandering groups of males – brothers or friends who have formed a coalition. Size and a formidable appearance are valuable assets in these battles, so male lions have developed impressive manes and have become considerably heavier than the females. But great size and weight make males less speedy and agile than the females, so they seldom take part in hunts. Usually they do no more than claim a share of the kills made by the lionesses of the pride, by using their greater weight and shouldering their way on to a kill once it has been made.

As the males age, so they lose strength. Eventually another group of wanderers will succeed in expelling them. When that happens the newcomers will kill any suckling cubs the females may have or any that any pregnant lionesses in the pride may produce within the next few weeks. The females will fight to protect their young but the males are bigger and more powerful than the females who cannot win.

Over a third of all cubs born in the pride are killed in this way. However, the bereaved females then become sexually receptive again very quickly, in weeks if not days, and breeding will start again. This may be one of the factors that produces the synchronicity in the females' sexual cycles. A minority of female cubs, as they approach adulthood, will leave the pride and seek a mate but most will stay with their mothers and their sisters. The male cubs however will be expelled before they are three or four years old.

So it is that large groups are very advantageous in lion society. The females need to stick together to claim and defend a hunting territory – and antelope and zebra are abundant enough to feed a number. Equally, a single male has to form a coalition to fight his way into a pride for he stands little chance of doing so by himself. So it may well be that lions have to live in large groups, whether or not team-work is necessary to bring down some kinds of prey.

There is corroboration of this. The ancestor of the domestic cat is the European wild cat that lives in the Middle East and Africa. Like most other cats, they are solitary creatures. But domesticated cats that have run wild, either in cities such as Rome or in farmyards, have found food on a scale that their wild ancestors never had. In farmyards, a cat needs no help in pouncing on a mouse. In a city centre, it needs no assistance in making a meal from the discarded remains of a chicken dinner. Team-work is not required.

In such places there is enough food to support great numbers of these ferocious feral hunters. But they do not all compete with one another

indiscriminately. They form teams. Females assist their sisters, daughters and even grand daughters. They live in close proximity with one another and band together to keep away any unrelated cats that seek to take up residence in their territory. They produce their kittens in a communal den and nursing mothers even allow their nephews and nieces to suckle. And tom cats living in smaller numbers alongside these female groups will kill the kittens fathered by their rivals. The parallel with lion prides is certainly a close one.

The fact that the kind of food a species eats will ultimately have a radical effect on its anatomy is demonstrable in every group of the mammals. But it also seems that even the abundance of that food may change an animal's character, even one that is as deeply ingrained as solitariness is in a cat.

Wild cat, Scotland △

6

THE OPPORTUNISTS

Bamboo is one of the most indigestible members of a markedly indigestible plant family. It is a giant grass. All grasses require particularly strong teeth to grind them and capacious stomachs, sometimes with special compartments, to digest them. Those mammals that developed such things and cropped grasses on the open plains of the world now flourish in vast numbers. But bamboo presents particular problems. It grows fifty feet tall and more. It is exceptionally tough and woody. Mature stems are so heavily impregnated with silica that they will blunt the sharpest and the strongest steel knife. Only its young shoots can be considered remotely edible. In consequence very few animals feed on bamboo. That means that any species that succeeds in doing so has vast quantities of food at its disposal. And that, it seems, is a great evolutionary inducement.

The giant panda's ancestors responded. Today the panda has large molar teeth that are flattened for crushing and grinding. Even the teeth that in cats are sharpened into carnassials, are shaped in this way. And it has a special device for harvesting the bamboo stems. No animals, except monkeys and apes, have thumbs that can bend towards other digits and so give a hand a grasp. Except for the giant panda. One of its wrist bones has become modified to form a projection, fully muscled and mobile, at the base of its front paw. This, in effect, gives it six digits on each of its front feet. By pressing this pseudo-thumb against the main pad of its foot, the panda can grip a young stem of bamboo and feed it into its mouth in the same way as one might eat celery.

But linking oneself so closely to a restricted diet is a risky thing to do. If for some reason that food disappears, an animal may be so specialised that it cannot switch to a different food and therefore starves. Bamboo has another unhelpful characteristic apart from its indigestibility. Some species flower only very rarely and extend their range instead by sending up shoots from the root-like rhizomes.

Giant panda feeding on bamboo, Sichuan, China ▷

But eventually, they do flower and all individual clumps of the same species do so simultaneously. Sometimes the period between flowering is fifteen years. In others it can be as long as a hundred and twenty. But after a species has flowered, all mature plants die. Its future now rests entirely in its seeds. If pandas were feeding in a forest of such bamboo, they would have to migrate after a mass flowering to find a different species. That, at the best of times, must have given giant pandas a recurring and serious problem. These days however, the increase in the human population of China has led to extensive felling of the bamboo forests. Few patches remain for pandas compared with only a century ago. If the bamboo in one of these small isolated sanctuaries dies off, the pandas – left to themselves – will die off too. It is hardly surprising that today the giant panda is one of the most endangered of all mammals. Specialism is a high-wire act – spectacular when it is successful but catastrophic if there is one small failure.

Yet it is possible for an animal to survive on food that appears only briefly and spasmodically if it is prepared – behaviourally, dentally, and digestively – to eat a great variety of widely different things. It can then feast on one food while that

happens to be available and when that disappears, move on to find a different one. That is the way of the omnivore and it was the one followed by most of the other members of the giant panda's family, the bears.

The biggest bear of all, the grizzly, lives in the far north of America. It is another of those species that has adapted to a cold climate by growing huge and thus conserving its body heat. The grizzly is immense. A big male can weigh over half a ton. It is also extremely fast and can easily out-run a man. Such stature, strength and speed make it a formidable hunter and grizzlies will kill mountain sheep and moose, the biggest of all deer. But prey of any kind can be energy consuming to find and kill, so meat is by no means the major element in their diet. In spring they eat all kinds of vegetation – grass, horsetails, skunk cabbage and lily roots. They wander down to the sea-shore and they scoop up molluscs from the sand. In summer they dine on elderberries and cranberries. They also dig out mice, squirrels and marmots from their burrows.

When the salmon start to migrate up Alaska's rivers, the bears gather beside falls and rapids, often in groups of a dozen or more, in places where they know that the salmon will have to leap in order to continue up-river and reach their spawning grounds. There, with great dexterity and perfect timing, the grizzlies snatch the jumping fish from the air. The rewards can be so great that in those special places where fish leap in great numbers, dozens of bears that normally avoid one another will gather together beside the falls and catch fish in their jaws without even moving.

The bears that live in Yellowstone have discovered a particular delicacy. In July, cutworm moths appear in thousands to feed at night on the summer flowers. During the day, they hide under rocks but the bears have discovered them and regularly climb up to altitudes of 10,000 feet in order to feast on them. A single bear in a single day will lick up 30,000.

But a big animal has a big appetite. That is one of the disadvantages of size and even such an unfussy omnivore as a grizzly may find it hard to get enough to eat. So grizzlies forage alone. When winter comes and the land is covered with a blanket of snow, even the enterprising and open-minded grizzly cannot find sufficient food to sustain itself. It solves the problem by going to sleep. Each bear, by itself, finds a cave or a hollow tree and settles down for slumber. Its bodily processes begin to slow. Its temperature drops several degrees and its pulse drops to about ten beats a minute. It becomes very drowsy. For the next five months it fuels its body from its fat reserves and does not eat or drink, urinate or defecate. This is not true hibernation like that of marmots, ground

159

Brown bear and her cub digging for clams, North America   *Brown bears fishing for salmon, North America* ▷

squirrels and other rodents, whose heart-beat at such times slows to almost imperceptible levels and whose temperature falls to within a degree or so of freezing. Such hibernators take considerable time to return to full activity. But it could be a serious mistake to suppose that sleeping bears in winter would behave in the same way. They can, if disturbed, rouse themselves instantly.

A female bear, however, may do more than sleep during the winter months. Even as she dozes, she gives birth. One, or more usually two, small naked cubs slip from her body. They are no bigger than rats, extraordinarily small compared with her huge bulk. A new-born human baby, which seems so minuscule to its parents, weighs about one fifteenth as much as its mother. The new-born grizzly is only about one hundredth. It is smaller, in proportion to the size of its mother than the young of any other placental mammal. But its tiny stature and total helplessness matters little, for here in a den in the middle of winter, in the furry embrace of its gigantic and powerful mother, nothing is likely to harm it.

For four or five months, the cubs remain with her in the darkness of the den, nourished by her milk and steadily growing. As the weeks pass, their eyes open, their fur appears and they grow bigger. Outside, the snow melts. And then, as spring arrives, the mother and her young emerge into the sunlight.

△ *Brown bears grazing, North America*

Now the cubs must eat something other than milk. At first, there are fresh green leaves and buds to eat, but as spring proceeds and temperatures begin to rise, new foods appear. Even intelligent and inquisitive young omnivores have to be taught about what can be found where, what is good to eat and what should be avoided. As each new crop appears, the mother grizzly guides her cubs to it. So they learn a precise sequence for their foraging. They will stay with her for another year or even two and go through the whole sequence again. After that they are on their own.

Farther north still, another bear, the white furred polar bear is not quite so open-minded about what it eats. An adult female behaves in much the same way as the female grizzly. When winter comes, she digs a den in the snow and there produces her cubs – again usually twins. She has little alternative, for her tiny naked young could hardly survive out in the open with temperatures dropping to 30°C below freezing. The males, however, have no such compulsion for they take no part in caring for the cubs. Indeed, there is every reason for them to remain active for there is a lot of food to be had out on the Arctic sea-ice.

Seals must breathe and throughout the winter they have to maintain holes in the ice where they can do so. A seal's breath certainly has a strong smell, but

Brown bear eating fruit, △

even so bears can detect it from extraordinarily long distances. They can identify the odour of a breathing hole from up to three miles away, even if it is buried beneath three feet of wind-blown snow. The bear will wait patiently beside such a hole and when the seal eventually appears, it uses its fore-paws to strike with such power that it may shatter the seal's skull. The seals are particularly vulnerable when breeding begins – from February onwards. The females haul themselves out alongside their holes and give birth usually in small chambers hollowed out beneath the snow. Bears are expert in locating these. They creep slowly towards them. If the female seal detects the hunter's approach she will slide down into the water and escape, but her pup for the first few days of its life, cannot swim. The bear rears up on its hind legs and brings its fore-feet down on the little

△ *Polar bear with seal kill, Norwegian Arctic*

cavern with devastating force. The pup is killed instantly. Male polar bears are well-fed throughout the winter.

When spring comes and temperatures rise, and life becomes easier for most of the inhabitants of the Arctic, polar bears paradoxically face more difficult times. The ice on which they roamed during the winter has disappeared. The bears are superb swimmers and can remain in the water continuously for many hours. Even so, they cannot swim for weeks on end. So now they come ashore. Here there is meat to be had but it comes in tiny units – ground squirrels and lemmings. These are minute helpings for a huge animal that a few months earlier was munching its way through pounds of seal blubber at a single sitting. But the polar bears, nonetheless, hunt for them with enthusiasm. Like the grizzlies, they also eat blueberries, cranberries and crowberries. They dig for roots and chew sedges. Even so, during the hard times of summer, they may need to draw on the fat reserves they accumulated during the winter days of plenty in order to survive. They may even get so desperate for meat that they will kill and eat cubs of their own species if their mothers do not keep them out of harm's way – and since they show no sign of recognising those they fathered, those cubs may be their own as well as those of others.

The smallest of the bear family, the Malayan sun-bear (its name refers to a yellowish blotch on its chest) is hardly bigger than a large dog. It is about as vegetarian as the polar bear is carnivorous and spends a great deal of its time climbing in trees, looking for fruit. But it is also particularly fond of honey and will rip apart tree-trunks to get at a nest of wild bees. Foraging down on the ground it eats all kinds of things. It scoops up eggs and nestlings of ground-nesting birds such as jungle fowl. It even tears open termite hills and licks up the soft-bodied larvae.

Other bears – the Asian black bear, the North American black bear and the Andean spectacled bear – are all similarly omnivorous, wandering through their territories snacking on whatever might be in season and whatever they might find. But one member of the family has started to specialise. The sloth bear is a particularly shaggy species that lives in the Indian subcontinent, from the foothills of the Himalayas in the north southwards across India to Sri Lanka. While it too takes a variety of animal and vegetable food, it has a particular taste for termites and it has already evolved special adaptations for collecting them. It has lost two of the incisors in its upper jaw and as a result has a gap in its front teeth. Its lips are naked and very large. And it has particularly big claws on its front feet. When it finds a termite hill, it first rips a hole in the side. Then it

pushes its snout into the hole, purses its lips to form a long tube and sucks. The termites are hoovered out of their chambers and corridors in hundreds. If the bear continues down this evolutionary road, it may eventually reach the tooth-less extremes of the giant anteater, and then another omnivore will have followed the giant panda out on to the high wire of specialism.

Omnivory was not, as one might think, the way in which mammals lived when they first appeared. The earliest mammals of all, which had tiny needle-like teeth could only have fed on insects. The first rodents, which were next to evolve, ate little other than nuts and fruit. They were followed by the leaf-eaters. It was not until some thirty million years ago that the first omnivores deserving of that name appeared. They were a branch of the cloven-hoofed forest-living family, typified by the chevrotains. The first of them were no bigger than terriers. Eventually, however, they became very large indeed.

Dinohyus, which flourished around twenty million years ago, was about the size of a hippopotamus and weighed around a ton. Its skull provides the clues

◁ *Spectacled bear feeding on puya, Andes*   *Sloth bear, India* △

about its life-style. Its front teeth were not chisel-shaped but short and blunt, so it cannot have been a specialised grazer like an antelope. Nor could it have been primarily a flesh–eater for its canines, though large, were not sharp or elongated into daggers. The molars at the back of its jaw however were very big with flattened tops, exactly what is needed to grind up vegetable matter – roots, fruit and leaves. In short, it had a set of generalised all-purpose teeth that could tackle most foods.

Its skull also provides clues to its habits. The shape of the inside of a cranium gives some indication of the form of the brain it once protected. Dinohyus's brain was not large for the size of its body, but it did have disproportionately big olfactory lobes. These are the parts of the brain that process signals coming along the nerves from the nostrils. That, together with the fact that the skull has a particularly long snout, suggests that Dinohyus had an acute sense of smell. And the skull has one further and rather strange odd characteristic. The underside of its jaws carries odd knobs and flanges. They indicate that this animal had some kind of facial decorations. All this suggests that this bizarre creature was an early member of the pig family.

Pigs are the least fussy of feeders. There is little that contains any sustenance whatever that a pig will not tackle. The wild boar of Europe eats almost anything

△ *Wild boar with young, Europe*

a woodland can produce — acorns, beech mast, chestnuts, ferns, earthworms, snails. frogs, mice, lizards, and carrion. It has a liking for truffles, an underground fungus that grows on the roots of oak trees a foot or so below ground, that virtually no other species (except mankind) thinks are worth eating and even human beings find difficult to locate. The forest-living European pig can detect them by their smell and grub them out with its strong snout. Peccaries, the South American branch of the pig family, readily eat cactus. In Africa, the bush pig is an enthusiastic rootler, ploughing up the ground with its nose and tusks seeking roots, corms and bulbs. The giant forest hog spends much of its time in grasslands and of necessity, grass dominates its diet. The red river hog lives in the rain forest and finds so many fallen fruits that it often eats little else. The warthog, on the other hand, lives on arid savannahs, and manages to flourish on roots and tubers, the leaf bases of grass and the bark of trees.

All these species of pig have a pair of teeth on either side of the jaw enlarged into tusks, some small, some very large indeed. These may be of help in digging up roots and excavating for truffles but it seems unlikely that this is their main function. The males use them when they fight one another and since they are usually bigger in males than females and vary in size and shape from one individual to another, it is likely that they also have something to do with

169

Warthog males fighting, Zululand △

courtship. But the fact is that all pigs, right from their earliest beginnings, seem to have a tendency to develop extravagant facial decorations. Dinohyus had those strange flanges on the underside of its skull that probably provided the basis for substantial fleshy growths of some kind. The African red river hog has spectacular moustachios. The warthog has a pair of flamboyant tusks, in each jaw but also 'warts', large skin-covered projections on each cheek which protect its eyes from the tusks of rival males when they do battle.

The most bizarre species of all is a pig that lives only on the island of Sulawesi in Indonesia, the babirusa. The tusks of the lower jaw of the male grow vertically upwards. Those in its upper jaw do the same but do not emerge from the side of the mouth. Instead they pierce the flesh of its snout and then curve backwards towards its forehead. Maybe female pigs of all species, ever since the family first appeared, have always had a fancy for facial decoration in their males.

Another family of early omnivores arose from a quite separate branch of mammals. They were an offshoot from the ancestral group that ultimately some ten million years later gave rise to the bears and the dogs. Those alive today are such an odd and varied collection that they don't even have a common family name. Technically, they are called procyonids, Procyon being the scientific name for their most familiar member, the raccoon. But others are much less well

△ Peccaries digging for salty minerals, Peru

Red river hogs, West Africa ▷
Babirusa boar, Sulawesi ▷

known – the olingo and the cacomistle, the coati, the kinkajou and – according to some authorities – the red panda. They all are about the size of a domestic cat; they all have long tails which, except for one, are ringed with black; and all – with one exception – are remarkably un-prejudiced about what they will eat.

If you are going to eat a great variety of things, it is as well to investigate them before you risk swallowing them, just to make sure that they are not poisonous or do not have a sting. The raccoon does this with its hands. It feeds mostly in the dark at night. The skin on its fingers contains a dense network of sensitive cells that enable the animal to detect the tiniest difference in texture. It can distinguish – by touch alone – the difference between a ripe and an unripe raspberry. It hunts for worms, listening carefully for the rustle they make as they feed in the leaf litter. Then it grabs one before it can totally withdraw into its hole and taking great care not to break the worm's soft body and so lose much of it, the raccoon delicately pulls it out of the ground. It feeds a great deal from streams and will sit on a bank groping in the water with its hands for crayfish, frogs and small fish. So deeply ingrained is this behaviour that in captivity raccoons dip the food that is given to them in their water bowls. This has led to a myth that they are concerned about the cleanliness of their food and wash it before they eat.

△ *Raccoon, Washington State*   *Brown coati, Costa Rica* ▷

The other relatively familiar procyonid is the coati. It seeks its food not with its hands but its nose which is long, narrow and very mobile. The coati sticks it into everything and it eats almost anything it discovers that seems even remotely edible – fruit and lizards, mice and spiders, millipedes and nestling birds. At one time there were thought to be two quite different kinds of this animal living in the same Central American forests. One, about the size of a terrier, lives in bands of up to twenty or thirty. Another, considerably bigger, is solitary. The local people called the first coati and the second coatimundi. In fact the bands of smaller ones consist of females with their daughters and half-grown sons. The large 'coatimundis' are all adult males. Nonetheless, both names are still used to describe the same single species.

A young male coati, as soon as it is adult, is expelled from its family group by the females. This is not an uncommon arrangement among mammals that live in small groups. Lions behave in this way and so do elephants. But remarkably, male coatis do not leave the group's territory. They simply forage alone, away from the others. Then the breeding season arrives. It only lasts for three or four weeks and all the females come into oestrus at very much the same time. At that point, the solitary males leave home and visit the territory of a neighbouring band. There they mate – after which the females expel them and they return to home ground.

Two other procyonids – the cacomistle and the olingo – are even smaller than female coatis. They live in trees and eat fruit, insects, birds and small mammals. A third, the kinkajou is very like them. Indeed it often associates with olingos in the tree tops and it can be quite difficult to distinguish between the two. But the kinkajou seems to have acquired a sweet tooth and that has already tempted it down the road to specialisation. Fruit forms about 90% of its diet. The remaining 10% of its food is made up of leaves, nectar and honey. So far, this sugary diet has had no effect on its dentition. Its teeth are still just as sharp as those of its fully omnivorous relations. The kinkajou however, uniquely among its group, has acquired a prehensile tail. This enables it to lean out from a branch to grasp a fruit that would otherwise be beyond reach. It also has an inordinately long tongue with which it can lick up nectar from the depths of flowers.

All these procyonids live in America. Only one, the little red panda, lives elsewhere. It is found in the forest of western China and the valleys of the eastern Himalayas. It is about the size of a raccoon but has beautifully soft red fur with cream patches on the side of its chest. Its odd distribution, away from all other procyonids is not the only reason to wonder whether it really belongs to this

Cacomistle, Mexico

group. It has another anomalous character too. Bamboo forms a major part of its diet and it has the beginnings of a pseudo-thumb, like the one that has been fully developed by the giant panda which lives alongside it in part of its range. These characters were reasons why the giant panda, when it was discovered by Westerners in 1869, forty years after the red panda had been described scientifically, was given its popular name. For a long time there was heated discussion about the correct systematic position of both these creatures. Some maintained that the two were so like one another and so unlike anything else that they should be given their own family, small though it would be. Today the relatively new science of molecular genetics has pronounced that the giant panda is indeed an aberrant bear and that the red panda is so different from true procyonids that it should be put in a group of its own. If that is so, then its possession of an incipient pseudo-thumb must be because both it and the black and white bear that we call the giant panda were both tempted by bamboo shoots. The same specialisation of diet in comparatively recent times has led them both to evolve the same kind of physical equipment with which to harvest it.

◁ *Olingo, Venezuela*
◁ *Kinkajou, Brazil*

Red panda, Himalayas △

Just as an omnivore may be tempted under some circumstance to become a specialist, so on occasion, a member of a specialist family given the right opportunity may widen its tastes to omnivory. The members of the weasel family are as dedicated to hunting as any mammal. Even so, force of circumstances has compelled one of them to widen its tastes. The wolverine lives in the Arctic. It is yet another example of an animal that has adapted to cold conditions by growing much bigger than its relations and thus increasing its ability to retain its body heat. Apart from size, however, it still has much the same kind of body as a weasel with sharp dagger-like teeth and short legs. It hunts reindeer. They, with their long legs and under good conditions, can easily outpace the squat, burly wolverine. But they cannot run fast through a deep snow-drift. They are so big and long legged that they sink in, often up to their bellies. The wolverine however has feet that are thickly furred and very wide so that its weight is spread over the surface of the snow, like that of a man wearing snowshoes. Consequently it can run over the surface of a snow-drift and catch and kill a floundering reindeer, usually by sinking its massive teeth into the base of its victim's neck. Such kills may be rare, so while meat is available the wolverine eats as much as it can. It will consume such phenomenal quantities of flesh at a single sitting that it has been given the alternative name of glutton. It is what you would expect of a giant weasel.

Even so, prey is scarce in the Arctic winter and the hunter has to be content with being a scavenger much of the time, eating from carcasses of those animals that have perished in the cold. In summer conditions are even more difficult, just as they are for the polar bear. Carrion is not so abundant. And a wolverine stands little chance of catching reindeer for they simply gallop away. So the glutton can no longer be gluttonous. It has to look for birds' eggs. It collects berries and digs for roots. It even snatches at flying insects. It has become an omnivore.

Dogs are true carnivores. Their carnassial teeth are proof of that. But some of them also take to omnivory under certain conditions. The maned wolf has such long legs that it looks like a fox on stilts. It stalks across the open grasslands of Brazil and Argentina searching for armadillos, rabbits, lizards and birds. Its great height, presumably, helps it to see and hear distant prey better than if it were submerged in the tall grass. But even with this advantage it cannot get as much as it needs and over half its food consists of plants, in particular the berries of a species of Solanum that it takes in such quantity that it is known as wolf fruit, *fruta da lobo*.

The most successful omnivore of all is not one that is descended from a long line of ancestral omnivores, but a recent recruit from the ranks of the rodents. It

Wolverine, northern Montana ▷

is the brown rat. Rats and mice have the sharp, continuously growing incisor teeth possessed by all rodents and most of the five hundred odd species use them in the same way, to chisel open seeds and nuts, scythe down grass stems, and gnaw roots. But the brown rat has been more adventurous. There seems to be no kind of vegetation that it will not touch, no part of a plant that it spurns. It eats other animals, dead and, on occasion, alive. Slugs, fish, and insects; beeswax, soap and cardboard boxes; meat, bone, hair, hide, guts, and toenails; all, in the eyes of the brown rat, are food. It will even tackle with apparent enthusiasm substances such as lead pipes, concrete and the plastic covering of electric cables. Brown rats, it seems, are compulsive feeders.

It might seem easy therefore, to control rats by poisoning them. That is far from being the case. They are extremely cautious about nibbling food they have not sampled before. If one eats poisoned bait that does not kill it but only makes it feel sick, it is able to link its indisposition to that unfamiliar taste even if it was sampled as much as twelve hours earlier and the rat had eaten other things in between. Not only that, if it encounters another rat that is ill and

△ *A maned wolf, Argentina*

smells an unfamiliar food on its lips, it will avoid that food. Equally, it is more likely to sample a new food if it smells it on the lips of an apparently fully fit rat.

Their vast appetite is coupled with rampant fertility. A female brown rat becomes sexually mature when she is eighty days old and produces a litter of about eight. She can do this virtually continuously. If all her young survive to breed as soon as they reach maturity, she can produce a thousand descendants in a single year And she can live for five years.

The consequences of such proliferation can be spectacular or horrific, according to the disposition of the observer. In India, rats are worshipped at a temple in Bikaner. Netting spread across the walls of the courtyards protects them from predatory birds. Worshippers come and give them grain. The rats seem to have no fear of anything. Visitors are required by religious convention to remove their shoes and the rats run heedlessly over their feet. They swarm up the pinnacles and burrow beneath the mattresses on which the priests who guard them sleep. Bearded holy men sit beside brass trays loaded with grain and share food with the rats which run in swarms over their shoulders and hide beneath their beards.

In the wild, a particularly vigorous individual male rat establishes a territory around the nests of a small group of females and drives off intruders. But when the population becomes particularly dense, as it has in the Bikaner temple, these rankings cannot be maintained. The population loses most of its social structure. When a female comes into oestrus, any male that can reach her will copulate with her. She may be mounted several hundred times in a single night. Rats then become a horde, a plague.

The brown rat is also known as the Norwegian rat. It is so-called because it was once believed that it reached Britain in the holds of Norwegian timber ships but that is almost certainly incorrect for it was first recorded in Britain in 1728 and was not seen in Norway until 1762. It is more likely that the British immigrants came from Russia. Within twenty years the species had driven out the slightly smaller and less aggressive black rat which seems originally to have been a tree dweller and tended to breed in lofts and between rafters. The brown rat however, is a burrower by nature. By the nineteenth century it had taken to the sewers of cities. There it found circumstances that suited it perfectly.

The sewers are warm in winter and cool in summer. They have well spaced gratings through which an animal can come and go as it runs along the sewers in search of food or new territories to colonise. And floating down the sewers

comes an endless, bountiful supply of discarded food, junk, refuse of all kinds, all of it, as far as the brown rat is concerned, potential food. Hardly surprisingly, by the end of the twentieth century, the brown rat had become one of the most widely distributed mammals in the world.

It owed much of its success to an alliance it had made, unilaterally, with another omnivore. This other species, like so many that follow such a way of life, has generalised unspecialised teeth that allows it to eat most things, and a digestive system that can deal with an unprecedented variety of foodstuffs. It also has a brain that gave it the intelligence to collect delicacies of every kind from all over the globe, to process kinds of food it could not otherwise either masticate or digest, and to cultivate in vast quantities those kinds of food that it particularly fancies. It was, of course, the most enterprising and widespread omnivore of all. Us.

◁ *A worshipper sharing food with rats,*
   Bikaner, India.

7

RETURN TO THE WATER

The waters of the world, whether salt or fresh, are full of food. That being so, you could hardly expect that animals as intelligent and enterprising as the mammals would ignore such a rich larder. Raiding it, however, is not easy for a four-legged, warm-blooded, air-breathing, live-bearing animal. Each one of those quintessential mammalian characteristics is an obstacle to life in the water. Nonetheless, over the course of the mammals' evolutionary history, representatives of the carnivores, the herbivores, and the omnivores have all made the move. Those that did so in the far distant past have now become so modified, so suited to a life in water, that their ancestral roots are barely identifiable, while others which are only just starting to sample such food have hardly changed.

A rat in the Congo is one of the most recent of them. Its fur, rich chocolate above and cream beneath, is so fine that its wearer is known as the velvet rat. This in itself is an adaptation to prevent chilling. Water conducts heat 25 times faster than air, so a warm body in water quickly has its heat sucked from it unless it is insulated in some fashion. Fur is one way of providing that protection. The velvet rat is certainly in need of it, for it spends a lot of time standing around in shallow pools deploying another adaptation – particularly long luxuriant whiskers. Standing on tiptoe, and holding its head close to the water, it spreads these whiskers across the surface. If it detects a ripple made by some small creature – a worm, a slug, a crustacean, a fish – moving in the water beneath, it dives in and swims after its prey trying to grab it with its forelegs. Having made its catch, it returns to dry land and settles down for its meal. Fine fur and long whiskers are only tiny adaptations but they are an example of these first small steps that a

species may take when it sets off down the evolutionary road towards an amphibious life.

Carnivorous mammals have made that journey several times during their history. Cousins of the weasels and polecats once did and became otters. The relationship between the two groups is easy to see, for otters, anatomically, are very like large weasels. Their sharp spiky canine teeth and shearing carnassials that served them so well on land are equally well suited to dealing with slippery fish. They have dealt with the problem of chilling in the same way that the velvet rat has done, by developing a very fine fur. Its outer layer is relatively coarse, being made up of long guard hairs. Beneath that, however, the fur is thick and so woolly that it traps air and forms very effective insulation indeed.

Swimmers, needless to say, use their limbs in a very different way from runners. The otters have converted their feet into paddles simply by growing webs of skin between their toes. They have also developed strong muscles at the base of the tail so that they are able to use it as a rudder. The need to breathe air, however, is still a major problem for them and they usually have to snatch a breath about every half-minute or so when they are in the water. Nonetheless,

European otter in a Scottish burn △

they are such skilled swimmers, so athletic and so bursting with energy, that even with this handicap, they can pursue and out-swim fish.

Although they have these very effective adaptations, most species of otter spend most of their lives out of water. During the day they are usually asleep in their dens beside a river bank. Even at night, when they do much of their fishing, they tend to rest on the bank for a few hours around midnight. Nor have they totally lost their skill or taste for hunting on land. In the Shetlands, where unusually they are almost as active in the day as in the night, they still catch rabbits. They also mark their territories with scent, as their weasel cousins do, leaving their droppings in little smelly piles on prominent rocks or tree stumps along the length of a river that an individual regards as its own. And the females still give birth on land, hidden away in their dens.

In Scotland, some otters live along the coast and regularly hunt in the sea. That causes them an additional though minor problem. If the sea water dries on their fur, the salt clogs their sweat glands, so when they return to land after a fishing trip, they usually wash themselves in the fresh-water that accumulates in small pools in the peat bogs.

One species of otter, however, spends all its life at sea. It lives all along the west coast of North America from Alaska to California and it has taken its adaptations for water-living several steps further. Sea otters have the thickest fur of any species in the family. Indeed, it is the thickest fur produced by any mammal, with a million filaments to the square inch. All the hairs on a human being's head number only about a tenth as many. To exploit the insulating potential of this fur to the full, sea otters spend time each day lying on the surface of the sea, blowing into their under-fur to ensure that it is always fully topped up with air. Their skin fits so loosely around their body that they can pull almost every part of it within reach of their mouths. Even so, living permanently in water saps a great deal of heat from an otter's body and it has to eat prodigiously into order to remain warm. Every day it consumes about a third of its own body weight. It is as if a human being, in order not to starve, has to eat a hundred hamburgers daily.

Individual sea otters vary a good deal in their tastes. Most, however, live on creatures that they collect from the sea floor – sea urchins, clams, abalone, crabs and oysters. They bring them up from considerable depths – 60 feet or so – and sometimes will make repeated dives to detach one from its moorings. If necessary they can descend as deep as 130 feet. When an otter finally brings up something edible, it also carries with it, packed into a pouch formed by the skin of its

armpit, a rock. Once on the surface it lies on its back, puts the rock on its stom-ach and then uses it like an anvil on which to smash open crabs and shellfish.

The scent glands that river otters and weasels use are no value to an animal that lives permanently in the water and the sea otter has lost them. Its hind legs have become so large and flipper-like that on the few occasions that one does haul itself out on to the rocks, it clambers about in a very clumsy way. But the modifications it has had to make in changing from a part-time swimmer to a full-time inhabitant of the ocean have been largely behavioural.

Remarkably, the animals are still territorial. In California, they live in coastal waters among marine forests of giant kelp. The plants are firmly attached to the sea floor but their huge straps rise to the surface and float along it. Here male sea otters establish their territories patrolling the borders and driving off intrud-ing males. To prevent themselves being carried away from their patch by ocean currents while they are asleep, they seize the free end of a kelp strap and then revolve in the water, so that the kelp wraps round them and they are firmly an-chored. Then they put their paws over their eyes and go to sleep. Even the ma-jor step of giving birth at sea has been achieved without substantial physical

Sea otter breaking open and eating a crab △

changes. The new-born babies cannot swim until they are about ten weeks old, but this causes them few problems. They are so fat and their fur is so woolly that they are naturally buoyant and when they are not lying on their mother's stomach drinking her milk, they loll about quite happily among the floating kelp straps.

The similarity between otters and weasels is so great there can be little doubt about the relationship of one to the other. Seals and sea-lions on the other hand have more debatable origins. Some authorities think that sea-lions are a branch of the weasel family that separated even before the weasels arrived at their defining identity. Other authorities maintain that both seals and sea-lions stem from early bear-like creatures.

Of the two, sea-lions retain marginally more of their land-living inheritance. They still have small external flaps to their ears which seals have lost. They swim by using their front legs which have been converted into very effective flippers. However, their hind legs, which also end in flippers and are very much shortened, can still be turned forward, so they are of some help in getting around on land. Indeed, a male sea-lion can move rather faster over a rough beach than a man can run. Seals, in contrast, propel themselves through the water not with their front limbs but their hind. These are now quite useless on land and the only way a seal can move when it is out of water is by a clumsy and ungainly humping of its whole body.

△ *Sea-otters resting in kelp bed*

Members of the sea-lion family also retain some of their fur. Indeed one group of them (known confusingly as fur seals) are so well clad that they were at one time intensively hunted for the sake of it. It is still waterproof but it loses much of its efficacy as insulation against heat loss if its owner dives to any depth for then the pressure of the water squeezes out the air. So seals, sea-lions and fur seals have a developed an additional protection – a layer of fat, known as blubber, just beneath the skin. In sea-lions it is relatively thin. Seals, however, have taken this adaptation somewhat farther. Their fur has been reduced to a thin layer of coarse hairs and their blubber may be as much as three inches thick.

There is a third sea-going mammal that clearly belongs to this group of swimming mammals – the walrus. It is immense. The bulls, which are bigger than the cows, may grow to a length of 10 feet and weigh a ton and a half. They share some anatomical characteristics with both seals and sea-lions. Like sea-lions, they are able to turn their hind flippers forward and so move with some speed over land; but like seals, they don't have external flaps to their ears. For this reason and other more technical ones, they have been given a family all to themselves.

Walruses live only in the Arctic. Great herds of them migrate southwards in the winter and return to the north when the weather warms in spring. Each year during these journeys, herds, hundreds strong, will haul out on particular traditional beaches and rest. Their blubber, which is as much as six inches thick, insulates them so efficiently that out of water, basking in the Arctic sunshine, they are at risk from overheating. The blubber, however, is pierced by blood vessels. As the animals warm up, so these vessels dilate, bringing blood close to the surface of the skin where it is cooled by the Arctic air. As a result the whole herd flushes pink, like incautious sunbathers. Underwater, the process works in the other direction and walruses appear to be almost white.

Walruses have a unique adaptation to a swimming life – an inflatable life-jacket. There are two large internal pouches on either side of the head, opening from the throat, that the animal can inflate with air from its lungs. Fully blown up each can contain a cubic foot of air and in the water they support the animal's head so well that a walrus can go to sleep at sea with no danger of its head slipping beneath the surface. These pouches may have another function too. The walrus, when courting, makes a wide range of underwater noises – clicks, knocks and rasping noises – which the huge air pouches amplify by acting as resonators.

Walruses feed mostly on clams and other bivalves that they dig up from the

Walruses hauled out on Round Island,
Alaska ▷▷

sea-floor. In the murky depths, several hundred feet down, there is little light – and during the long Arctic winter, none at all – but the walrus's bulbous snout carries a spectacular array of stout bristles with which it is able to feel its way across the sea bottom and identify things to eat. It used to be thought that the animals dug out clams with their tusks, which in males may be three feet long. Now it is believed that this is not the case. They excavate their food from the muddy sea floor by squirting jets of water from their mouths. The tusks' primary function seems, instead, to be to indicate strength and seniority within a herd in rather the same way as the horns of goats do. Even so, the tusks can have a quite practical use. Walruses have been seen to use them like ice-picks, jabbing them on to the edge of an ice flow in order to help in hauling themselves out of the water.

Breathing below the surface remains a limitation for seals, sea-lions and walruses, but all have greatly improved on the best an otter can do. The danger faced by a human air-breathing diver is that air taken into the lungs under pressure will dissolve in the blood. Then, when the diver returns to normal pressures, that air will emerge again and form bubbles in the blood vessels. They will then cause

△ *Bull elephant seal underwater, California*   *A fur seal diving, Galapagos* ▷

the affliction known as the bends which may well lead to paralysis and death. Seals and sea-lions, however, have exceptional quantities of haemoglobin in their blood. This is the chemical that absorbs oxygen and transports it to the tissues. In addition they have unusually large amounts of another substance, myoglobin, within their muscles which also absorbs oxygen in a similar way. That means that they are able to hold within their body much more oxygen than most land-living mammals can. So, when a seal or a sea-lion starts to dive, it can empty its lungs of air, which pours from its mouth as a stream of silver bubbles. It then has a particularly large store of oxygen in a non-gaseous form in its haemoglobin and myoglobin. Even so it is extremely economical in its use. It restricts the flow of its blood so that oxygen is only delivered to the organs that are essential for life, such as the heart and the brain. To reduce its energy consumption its heart slows to a few beats a minute. With these physiological modifications a fur seal can dive to 650 feet and remain submerged for five minutes. The biggest of the seals, the southern elephant seal, almost unbelievably, can swim down to four thousand feet and not come up again for almost two hours.

Neither seals nor sea-lions, however, have managed to solve the problem of giving birth at sea and that inability has a profound effect on their social lives. A beach, to be suitable for them as a nursery should be smooth and sandy. It should be protected from heavy breakers. The sea floor leading up to it should have a gentle slope so that coming ashore is easy. And it should be safe, as far as possible, from land-living predators, either because it lies on a remote island or because it is enclosed on the land-ward side by tall unscaleable cliffs. Such beaches are not necessarily common and may have to accommodate seals and sea-lions coming from all over great expanses of open ocean. So in the breeding season they are usually greatly overcrowded.

The males arrive first. Sea-lion males are big and ferocious and fight among themselves to establish territories along the beach. These battles are very vicious indeed. The males still have the dagger-sharp canines inherited from their land-living carnivore ancestors and they fight by slashing at one another's necks. A great deal of blood is spilt. Small young males stand no chance of winning and are driven to the margins of the territories or to neutral ground at the head of the beach. The victors, the beachmasters, then sit in the middle of their estates, glowering belligerently around. This kind of warfare inevitably puts a premium on size and strength and male sea-lions are as much as five times the weight of the females.

The females arrive within two weeks or so later. They are pregnant with

young that were conceived a year earlier, almost certainly on this beach. Within a few days of landing, they give birth. Soon after that each becomes sexually receptive once more. This is the moment a beachmaster has been waiting for and he pounces on her. Copulation seems a cruel affair. He is so much bigger and heavier than she is. After this ordeal, she goes to sea and feeds, returning from time to time to suckle her pup. The beachmasters, however, do not leave. They have a compulsion to copulate with as many females as possible. On land, there is no food for them. The breeding season lasts for two to three months. By the end of it, the beachmasters, that were recently so heavy and muscular are almost skeletal.

The majority of true seals however, do not breed on land but on ice. There, they find all the space they require and there is no need for them to crowd together. Their breeding arrangements consequently are very different. Out on the flat emptiness of ice it would be very difficult for a male, no matter how big and powerful he is, to maintain a harem or patrol a territory. On the ice, each female must be competed for individually.

Crab-eater seals in the breeding season lie out on the sea ice in pairs, each

195

Male sea-lions fighting, Galapagos △

beside a pup. Each group, however, is not, as one might wish to believe, a devoted family with the male loyally staying beside his partner ready to help to protect their joint offspring. He is there ready to mate with the female just as soon as she stops providing milk for her pup. The baby is of no concern to him for it was conceived a year ago and has some other father. His very presence seems to be enough to deter any other male from having designs on the female and there is rarely any violent confrontation.

The hooded seal male is more demonstrative. He has a bladder on his nose and another on top of his head. The two are interconnected and as he lies beside his female, he lazily blows air from one to the other. If another male approaches however, he inflates both at the same time so that they come together and form a large black hood twice the size of a football. As the intruder gets closer, the resident shuts one nostril and blows down the other, inflating a nasal membrane into a gigantic scarlet balloon. He then shakes it violently from side to side so that it makes a pinging noise. That usually is enough to dissuade any intruder from persisting.

The hooded seal, the crab-eater and most other kinds of seal copulate out of

△ *Crab-eater seal pup suckling, Antarctica*

the water so it is not difficult for a male, when the moment comes, to impose himself upon a female. Another northern hemisphere seal, however, has managed to break this male dominance. Female harbour seals give birth on beaches but instead of copulating there, they mate in water. There they cannot be corralled into groups as they can be on a beach, nor claimed by a dominant male lying alongside them on an ice floe and seeing off his rivals. In the open three-dimensional world of water, they can easily dodge males if they wish. Now it is up to the males to entice them.

The males assemble in groups just offshore waiting for a female who has finished suckling to swim by on her way to the open sea. As soon as one approaches, a male swimming nearby starts to make a low rumbling call that sets his neck quivering. It gets louder and louder and eventually ends with a huge crash. It is not certain whether this underwater roaring is directed primarily at other males, trying to frighten them away or whether it is a way of demonstrating that the performer is the fittest individual around and the best possible father for a female's young. It is followed by even more extraordinary submarine behaviour. Other males arrive and join the calling male. They place their

Male hooded seal displaying his balloon △

muzzles on his and lying in a rosette they too start singing, as amicably as if they were all the members of a close-harmony group.

The full explanation of this amazing performance is not yet known but it seems that the male who initiated it is the dominant individual in the whole group. If the female is impressed, she will mate, and her partner will be the male who took the lead in the proceedings. What the rest of the singers gain from their contribution is uncertain.

Herbivores too have been tempted into the water, for there are plenty of plants to be cropped there. Sea-cows – dugongs and manatees – do so. It is very difficult indeed to imagine exactly what their ancestors might be. A manatee's superficial appearance gives few clues. Its sack-like hairless body, about ten feet long, has a broad spade-shaped tail at one end and a luxuriant bristly moustache at the other. Its front legs have been turned into short paddle-like flippers but it has lost its hind limbs entirely. It has two circular discs on its forehead that can be retracted to expose nostrils, and two small wrinkled depressions on either side of the head that show the position of its tiny eyes.

Even its internal anatomy is not very helpful. It has flat peg-like molar teeth which, as they are ground down, slowly migrate along the jaw and are replaced

by new ones which erupt at the back and slowly move forward. It has only six vertebrae in its neck – which is fewer than any other mammal. It has an extremely long gut with a side extension, the caecum, but it does not have a specialised chambered stomach like a ruminant. So its ancestral connections remain mysterious.

It seems most likely that both manatees and dugong sprang from the same stock as that which produced elephants. One thing is certain. They were, as their extreme adaptations suggest, among the very first of the mammals to take to the water for fossils of ancestral manatees that still retain their legs have been found which date back fifty million years to the time when the mammals were only just beginning their expansion after the disappearance of the dinosaurs.

It may be that the first of the sea-cows made their move, not into the sea but into fresh water, for there green plants are rather more abundant. Today, manatees live in the Amazon and the swamps and winding streams of Florida as well as in African rivers. In the West Indies, they also crop marine plants along the coast. The dugong however, is entirely marine and lives in the south-west Pacific and the Indian Ocean.

A sea-cow's life is not a demanding one. The waters they inhabit are shallow and warm. They trundle through underwater meadows, propelled entirely by slow, downward sweeps of their huge tail, leaving long trails behind them. Since they live on plants and plants need light in order to grow, they have no reason to swim to any depth. They are so big that few other swimmers can attack them and sharks only seldom venture into these shallow waters. Their upper lip is well furnished with muscles. That of the manatee is split and so mobile that the animal can grasp leaves with it, rip them up and push them into the mouth. The dugong's upper lip is disc-shaped and is used to grub up the rhizomes of sea grass from the sandy sea-floor.

Dugongs off the tropical coasts of Australia live in scattered herds and tend to patrol the same paths through their pastures cropping only the young sprouts along the verges which are tender and more nutritious than the old growth. Their life, in fact, seems to be as uneventful and monotonous as that of a herd of domestic terrestrial cows, until that is, the beginning of the breeding season. Then a few of the males may get uncharacteristically excited and start slapping the surface of the water with their tails. This seems to be a signal for all to head for deeper waters. The females do not all come into breeding condition simultaneously, so when one does, all the males begin to take interest in her. Fights

◁ *Manatee, Florida*

break out. The water boils with thrashing tails and lunging bodies. Eventually one male wins and mates with the female, belly to belly.

When the young is eventually born, it suckles from a nipple in its mother's armpit. Since it and its mother are, of course, air-breathing the mothers may at this time rear out of water, to allow their drinking young to breathe. It is this, some say, that gave rise to legends of the mermaid. That, bearing in mind that the mother's face is heavily moustached but otherwise featureless, seems a little unlikely. It is nonetheless true that science named the whole group sirenians, after the Sirens, the sea nymphs whose seductive singing lured sailors on to the rocks – and that seems even more unlikely.

Ancient though the dugongs are, another group of mammals moved into the seas at about the same time. These pioneers are thought to have sprung from the same branch that also gave rise to hippos. They made the move around fifty million years ago and in an astonishingly short time – a mere twelve million years – evolved adaptations for life in water that are the most extreme and the most perfect achieved by any mammals. They are the whales.

The blue whale is the biggest animal of any kind that has ever existed on

△ *Dugong feeding, Vanuatu, South Pacific*

earth. The largest of the dinosaurs is thought to have weighed around 100 tons. The blue whale can grow to lengths of 110 feet and weights of 190 tons. It is not surprising that a sea-living creature should exceed the weight of any terrestrial animal for bone is simply not strong enough a material to carry such immense weights. In the sea, however, water supports an animal's body and bones do no more than provide its framework.

The whale's body is streamlined to perfection. It is entirely shrouded by a blanket of blubber which in places is twenty inches thick. Its forelegs have become long slender flippers. Its hind limbs have disappeared altogether except for small relict bones buried within its flanks. It has no external ears and no external genitals.

Until very recently, blue whales were among the most elusive animals in the sea. They are solitary and cruise at up to twenty knots on unpredictable courses through the immensities of the open ocean, so encountering one was largely a matter of luck. But now scientists have perfected techniques that can take observers to within a few yards of these immense animals. Painstaking observations have begun to reveal their traditional migration routes. A slow-flying aircraft circling several hundred feet up for hours at a time over likely stretches of ocean, will with luck be able to spot one in the clear blue seas even though it is fully submerged. Radio calls from the air to a fast launch can direct it to roughly the right patch of water. Once there, a fast rubber dinghy can leave the launch and head at speed towards a distant spout as the animal surfaces to breathe. A skilled helmsman, knowledgeable about whale behaviour, can then judge where the cruising whale may next come up to breathe and take you there.

You look over the side and if you are lucky, the sapphire blue of the Pacific water will begin to pale. You realise that something flat, horizontal and vast is slowly rising from the depths towards the surface. It's the whale's tail. You look ahead, seventy feet, almost the length of a tennis court, and a grey hump breaks the surface with the waves swilling over it. It is so far away that it hardly seems possible for it to be connected to the flat white shape still rising beside your dinghy. A pair of nostrils opens in the distant hump and with a whoosh, a plume of vapour blasts thirty feet into the sky. Fishy-smelling droplets of mucus may fleck your face. The whale is idling. Even so it is sliding through the water so swiftly the dinghy can barely keep up with it. The whale's head may rise and spout a few more times but then the tail breaks the surface and rears up into the air, dripping with water. It is as wide as the wing of a small aircraft. The next

dive the whale makes will be a deep one. It may be gone for an hour and you can have little idea of where it will have travelled to in that time. Your encounter is over.

The blue whale, the biggest of all animals, lives on some of the smallest – krill, small shrimp-like crustaceans a couple of inches long. It captures them, millions at a time by opening its jaws and distending its pleated throat so that its mouth fills with water. It then half shuts its jaws and expels the water by pushing forward its gargantuan fleshy tongue. A blue whale's tongue is as big as an elephant. This forces the water out of its mouth through a line of bristle-fringed horny slats, the baleen, that hang from the whale's toothless upper jaw. The krill is left behind to be swept off the baleen by the tongue and then swallowed.

No environment on land can parallel the conditions in which these mammals live. They move freely in three dimensions. Uninterrupted water may stretch horizontally around them for hundreds of miles. Below them it reaches downwards for maybe a mile or more into inky blackness. In such watery emptiness, how do these mammals navigate around the globe to find their food or one another? They probably have a reasonable sense of taste that enables them to savour

△ *Surfacing blue whale, Baja California*   *Grey whale feeding on krill, California* ▷

the faint traces of chemical ingredients that might distinguish different parts of the ocean, but that is likely to be of only limited value in feeding or reacting with one another.

They also have eyes, but these are very small and can be of little use under most circumstances for even in clear water it is not possible to see great distances and at depth, of course, eyes are no use at all.

But they can hear. Whales do not have external ears and the opening of the ear canal, even in the biggest of whales, is tiny, no more than a centimetre in diameter. But their hearing, nonetheless, is acute. Sound travels further and faster in water than it does in air. A loud noise in the sea can be heard without undue distortion hundreds of miles away. So they must be able to pick up the distant thunder of waves breaking on a shore, the high pitched snaps and twitterings of crustaceans, the sound of marine engines and revolving propellers. It now seems that they can navigate by sonar, as bats do, but on a vastly greater scale. A blue whale travelling south through the North Atlantic seemed to be bouncing its calls off the continental shelf of Northern Ireland. But above all, they can hear one another.

Baleen whales, in particular the humpback, a smaller cousin of the blue

whale, exploit sound to the full in organising their social life. During the breeding season, the males hang in mid-water producing long sequences of sounds – deep moans, whoops, soaring glissandi, high squeaks and staccato grunts. Several humpback whales, separated from one another by miles of water may be singing at the same time. What is more all those in the same population will be singing the same phrases in the same sequence. But each individual makes his own decision as to how many times he repeats each component phrase before he moves on to the next in sequence. A complete song may last for ten minutes and a whale may repeat it continuously for twenty-four hours at a time. It seems that female humpbacks, like female birds, use these songs as a basis for selecting their mates.

The males also display by smacking the surface of the sea with their flippers and even leaping clear of the water and landing, all fifty tons, on the surface making a noise like a cannon shot. When females do appear, rival males may fight and barge one another as they surround her. Copulation, when it finally occurs, lasts only a minute or so.

The young are born about a year later. As an infant emerges from its mother, she nudges it to the surface to take its first breath. Then it drinks. A slit in her side opens and a nipple protrudes. The baby grabs it with its mouth and the mother squirts out milk by contracting a muscle that encloses her milk store. This milk is extremely rich containing 46% fat. The richest cow's milk contains about 5%. Young blue whales are said to double their birth weight in seven days. It takes a human baby about 120 days to do so. The last of the mammals' obstacles to a completely marine life, giving birth at sea, has at last been overcome.

Another group of the early pioneering whales took to a different way of feeding. Instead of losing their teeth and replacing them with a sieve of baleen strips, they retained them. The earliest species had teeth which were differentiated into incisors, canines and molars. These, however, changed in later species to a uniform array of simple pegs, sometimes with a backward curve to them, which are ideal for grabbing the slippery bodies of fish. The most primitive of these toothed whales alive today are the dolphins that swim in some of the world's great rivers, the Ganges and the Indus, the Yangtze and the Amazon. They are tiny compared to the huge baleen whales, none being more than nine feet long. Their neck bones, which in other dolphins have become fused together are still separate so they can move their heads from side to side and the bones of their fingers are still distinguishable and separate within the gristle of their flippers.

The Ganges dolphin lives in waters that are so cloudy and thick with

suspended mud that no one swimming in it, animal or human, could see more than a few inches ahead. The dolphin certainly cannot, for it is blind. Its eyes are tiny and do not even have lenses within them. The animal finds its way around by moving its mobile neck from side to side and making a series of clicking noises. These sounds are very high-pitched and, like those produced by bats, have important components that are far beyond the range of the human ear. They are produced in passages within the skull and then focussed, amplified and transmitted forward by a large lump of fat on the dolphin's forehead known as the melon. When the beam of these ultra-sounds strikes a hard object, they are reflected back as echoes and received by another lump of fat in the lower jaw, which extends upwards towards the dolphin's ear. So even though the animal is blind, it has a detailed mental picture of its surroundings.

The Ganges dolphin feeds in its own peculiar way, tipping on its side and ploughing its flipper through the mud, stirring it up in clouds. As it does so, it greatly increases the frequency of its clicks so that, converted down into our audibility, they sound like the chatter of a machine gun. The effect for the

205

River dolphin, South America △

dolphin must be like shining a torch in the twilight and it enables the animal to locate and snap up crabs, shrimps and bottom-living catfish.

All toothed whales, large and small – dolphins and porpoises, pilot whales, bottle-nosed whales and killer whales, over seventy different species in all – use sounds, not only to find their way around and locate prey but to communicate with one another.

The bottlenose dolphins that live off the coast of South Carolina form small groups of half a dozen or so and come inshore to fish in the winding channels that run between the low flat islands fringing the coast. At low tide, the falling water exposes narrow strips of mud between the water's edge and the reed beds beyond. The dolphins swim back and forth in a rough semicircle from one end to another of such a mud-bank, moving closer and closer towards it. Then, with perfect synchronisation they suddenly come together to form a line abreast with their flanks almost touching, and charge towards the mud-bank, driving shoals of small fish ahead of them. They swim so fast and with such power that they create a bow wave that sweeps them and the fish right out of the river and up on to the mud. As the water drains away, the dolphins roll over on their flanks and snap up the fish with the sides of their mouths. They all turn in the same direction –

always on to their left flank, though no one knows why. If they did not, then two next to one another would be trying to catch the same group of fish while those fish they had turned their backs on would be missed. Then the dolphins, flapping their bodies energetically, wriggle back into the water and swim further up the river to repeat the performance on another mud-bank. As they approach it, one of them will usually spy-hop, rearing out of the water taking a good look at the above-water world, perhaps to make sure that no danger lurks around the site of their next attack.

It is not easy to predict where that will be. You can easily see which of the mud-banks ahead, on either side of the river, is of the right sort of size, but that is not the only basis of judgement for the dolphins. No doubt they must also assess the shape of the river-bed that leads up to it, judge whether the tide is at the most suitable level and whether there are enough fish nearby. You yourself cannot see these things from a boat. But the seagulls flying overhead will give you a clue. A small group of them regularly follows each dolphin hunting party, hoping to steal a share of their catch. They know the river and the dolphins better than you do. Twenty feet up in the sky, they may also be able to

207

◁ *Bottle-nosed dolphins, Red Sea*   *Bottle-nosed dolphins catching fish by stranding,* △
South Carolina

see exactly where the dolphins are heading, in spite of the murkiness of the water. If you want to photograph the action, you would be wise to follow the gulls' lead. But even then they sometimes get it wrong. They will fly ahead and assemble on the next likely mud-bank only to see the dolphins veer away from it and surge up the mud on the other side of the river. If the dolphins always hunted in the same places in the same sequence, no doubt the gulls would have learned by now what it was. The dolphins are clearly making judgements according to the circumstances of the moment.

How do they agree between themselves on the next site for an attack? How does the spy-hopper communicate to the rest of the group that it is safe to do so – if indeed that is what it is doing? Above all, how are they able to understand one another's intentions so perfectly that, in an instant, they stop swimming back and forth herding the fish and come together to rush simultaneously towards the bank.

There is little doubt that they do so with sound. In addition to their high-frequency echo-locating calls, dolphins make a great range of whistles and squeaks that are well within our own hearing and can be picked up by a hydrophone. Dolphins, indeed, are among the most vocal of mammals. Their calls enable the members of a group to maintain contact with one another even in the open ocean when individuals may be widely scattered. They can hear one another's calls at distances of at least half a mile. Each animal has its own distinctive call-sign, known as a signature whistle, which is incorporated into these vocalisations. The dolphins can tell from this which of their companions they are hearing. There is even a possibility that one individual can attract the attention of another by, as it were, calling it by name. Exactly how much information they can convey to one another is not clear. Human beings can certainly train them to understand very complicated instructions so it is possible that teams communicate with one another in quite complex ways. Research is still continuing on how sophisticated this language is.

Mammals first took to water to find food. There was plenty of it there – fish, molluscs, crustaceans, plants. But today there is a greater variety than ever before. Now there are other mammals. Grey whales are 40 foot long filter-feeders. Every spring those in the eastern Pacific assemble in the warm shallow lagoons of Baja California off the coast of Mexico. Here the females give birth to their calves. In the spring, they begin a long journey up the western coasts of north America to the Arctic where they will feed on the burgeoning numbers of shrimps, worms and other invertebrates that swarm in the sediment of the sea

floor. The males and non-breeding females lead the way, travelling at around 4 knots. The journey north is six thousand miles long. The young whales cannot tackle it until they are several months old, so the last to leave are the females with young. They will be travelling slowly for a calf can only swim half as fast as an adult. Off the coast of California, pods of killer whales lie in wait for them.

Killer whales are normally very vocal but when they detect the approach of a grey whale and her calf they fall silent. They start to follow the pair. Before long the whale and her calf become aware that they are being chased. The mother increases her speed, encouraging her calf to swim as fast as it can, but the killers have no difficulty in keeping up. They take turns in harassing the calf. They have to be careful, for the female could severely injure them with a blow from her tail. After three or four hours, the calf is so exhausted that it can go no further. The killers force themselves between it and its mother. Once it is separated, the killers swim over it, forcing it downwards, preventing it from breathing. Eventually, the calf drowns and the killers make their meal. Often all they eat is the tongue. The rest of the body is left to sink slowly to the sea floor.

△ *Killer whale spy-hopping, Antarctica*   *Killer whales attacking grey whale and calf* ▷ ▷

The parallel between such killer whales and the packs of lions preying on wildebeest and their calves as they migrate across the African savannahs is an obvious one. Mammals have become so at home in the sea that now the ancient duels that they have fought between themselves for so long on land are being continued, even in the remote waters of the open ocean.

△ A pod of killer whales, Alaska

8

LIFE IN THE TREES

A hungry inquisitive animal, searching for food in a forest, turning over the leaf litter, sniffing in holes, pulling off bark, must soon have its attention drawn upwards. If it is an insect eater, it may have been tracking a column of termites snaking across the ground only to see them suddenly climb vertically up a tree trunk and disappear into the branches above. If it was searching for leaves, it must have noticed soft succulent ones just above its reach. Fruit-eaters must look greedily at brightly coloured, sweet-smelling fruits dangling overhead. If and when any animal, attracted by such temptations, does manage to clamber up there, it will indeed find great rewards. Armies of succulent caterpillars are munching their way through the aerial pastures. Pupae wrapped in silken cocoons are tucked into crevices of the bark. Small frogs can be picked out from the chalices of the vase-plants that sit on the branches. There are lizards and snakes to be caught, and eggs to be collected from birds' nests. So all kinds of mammals climb.

Some are still not very good at it. In northern Australia and New Guinea, unlikely though it may seem, a kangaroo makes the attempt. Its hind legs hardly seem suitable. They are long and powerful and excellent for making great leaps, but not very versatile. Its long tail may serve as a counterbalance as it does on the ground, but it does little else and in the trees, it seems more of a nuisance than a help. So the tree-kangaroo climbs rather cautiously. It moves along branches with alternate steps of its hind legs. Sometimes if the branch is particularly broad, it risks a few hops with its forelegs tucked against its chest. These are short but nonetheless just long enough to allow it to embrace a tree-trunk if necessary. Coming down, it always goes tail-first, clinging tight with its forelegs while slithering with its back legs until it is about six feet from the ground. Then it kicks against the trunk and twists round in the air so that, if it is lucky, it lands upright in the posture proper to a kangaroo. Sometimes, its descents are even more undignified. When alarmed and trying to rush away

through the canopy, it often loses its footing altogether and tumbles to the ground. If there were any sizeable meat-eating mammals in the forests where it lives – which there are not – the tree-kangaroo would surely not survive for long.

Most mammals that have taken to the trees, however, are rather more successful and agile. They deal with the problems of getting around safely in several different ways. Some, separately and independently, have evolved an adaptation that, so far, has eluded the tree-kangaroo. They have developed a grasping tail. The vertebrae near its tip have become particularly numerous and shorter than they are near the base so it is very mobile. The muscles on its underside are also bigger and stronger than those on the upper. These two modifications enable an animal to wrap its tail round a branch and grip it so firmly that many who have such a tail can support the weight of their bodies with it.

The binturong is one of these. It is a civet that lives mostly on fruit high up in the canopy of the forests of South-east Asia. It looks like a yard-long black hearth rug and is so supremely confident in its aerial domain that it moves in a very leisurely way, plucking a fruit or a leaf here and there, and often does so hanging beneath a branch as happily as it does clambering above it.

◁ *Tree-kangaroo, New Guinea*   *Binturong, Malaysia* △

In South America anteaters have taken to the trees. The tamandua is a smaller version of the ground-living giant anteater. Its tail, however, is very different. It is prehensile and instead of being covered with long shaggy hair like the giant's, it is only thinly furred. The pygmy anteater is less than a foot long, with a pale furry body. When this species is alarmed, it wraps its tail round a branch and rears up on its hind legs, waving its front-legs with their curved claws at what it myopically sees as its enemy. The kinkajou, a relative of the

◁ *Tamandua, Guyana*

Pygmy anteater in defensive posture, △
South America

raccoon, has a similar prehensile tail which it uses to secure itself as it leans out to pluck fruit. The rodents have also produced a prehensile-tailed tree-climber – the South American tree-porcupine that feeds on shoots, leaves and fruits. It is the only placental animal with a tail that coils upwards. Accordingly the pad of tough skin, free of spines, that gives the tail its grip, is on the upperside.

Clambering around, anchoring yourself with a grasping tail when necessary, may be safe, but it can sometimes mean going a very long way round to reach a meal. Fruit in the canopy of a neighbouring tree may only be a few horizontal yards away, but getting to it may involve descending one tree, making a long and possibly hazardous trip across the ground and then climbing up another. If you can jump, you can take a short cut. The European red squirrel takes this option if it can. A leap of four yards – a considerable distance for such a small animal – is not beyond it.

△ *Tree-porcupine, Guyana*   *European red squirrel jumping* ▷

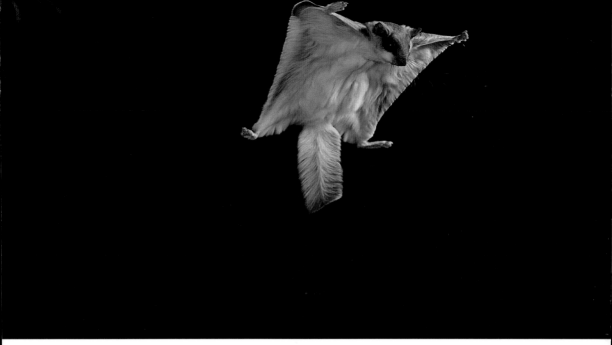

In America, some squirrels are even more accomplished acrobats. They can cover fifty yards in a single leap – by gliding. Before they take off they lean forward looking hard at a possible landing point ahead, swaying from side to side, perhaps to assess just how far away it is. Then they launch themselves into the air, stretch out their four legs, spreading a sail of skin that extends from their wrists to their ankles and they glide. Their long furry tail trails behind them, acting as a rudder and they can bank and turn by adjusting the position of their arms and legs, so varying the tension of their gliding membrane. As they near their chosen trunk, they brake, swinging their tail and body upwards so that they land facing up. They then gallop up the trunk and regain the height they lost during the glide.

American flying squirrels are about the same size as their European non-gliding cousins. In Asia, however, some flying squirrels are giants with bodies, not counting the tail, some eighteen inches long. They can glide for a hundred yards or so. They live in holes in tree trunks and are so at home among the branches that they seldom, if ever, descend to the ground. Their ability to glide as well as this, however, comes at a price. The gliding

◁ Flying squirrels, North America

Flying squirrel in flight, △
North America

membrane, when its owner tries to run, is so big it is something of an encumbrance. The Asiatic giant, lolloping along a branch, looks as though it is wearing a voluminous cloak. It is not surprising, therefore, that flying squirrels seldom come out of their holes during the day when there are eagles and other predators around that could pounce on them. In the evenings, however, they will emerge and in the gathering dusk put on an unforgettable display of aerobatics as they chase one another from branch to branch and tree to tree.

The most accomplished glider of all, however, is another South-east Asian animal, the colugo. It is about the size of a cat. Its gliding membrane stretches not just from wrists to ankles but to the tips of both its fingers and toes, half way up its neck and to the very end of its tail. With the help of this, it can cover 70 yards in a single graceful and silent glide. It is, from all accounts, exclusively vegetarian. The fur on the upper side of its membrane is particularly handsome, dappled with cream or brown blotches each ringed with black that conceal it very effectively as it nestles in the centre of palm trees or hangs below a branch with all its four feet placed close together. Its floppy gliding membrane is so big, and its

△ *Colugo in flight, Borneo*

slender legs so extremely adapted to serve as lightweight struts for that membrane, that on the ground it is virtually helpless.

But what kind of animal is it? Its teeth, that in most mammals normally provide valuable clues in establishing affiliations, are of no help for they are quite unlike those of any other living creature. The incisors of the top jaw are placed at the sides leaving a gap at the front and the second of them has, uniquely among mammals, two roots. The incisors on the lower jaw are even stranger. They project not up but forward and are toothed, like combs. Whether the colugo uses these to groom itself or to help it feed in some way is still not known. But although no living animal has teeth that are comparable, fossil skulls with very similar dentition are not uncommon in shales and sandstones laid down some 60-70 million years ago in North America. It seems that the colugo is the last living representative of a very ancient and successful group that appeared just as the mammals were beginning their expansion.

At around the same time, a group of insectivores related to the shrews were also experimenting with flight, using a different technique. The primary support for their membranes were the fingers of their hands. This arrangement allowed them to retain the full movement of their shoulder joints. They could flap. They were the insect-eating bats which have already been described. Today, however, there are other bats in the skies that are much bigger than the insectivorous ones. These are the fruit bats.

They are very different from the insect-eaters. Their food is largely if not entirely fruit. None of them has the highly sophisticated apparatus in their ears and noses that enables them to find their way by sonar – though one species does get some guidance from its low frequency calls. They navigate instead by sight. The large eyes that enable them to do so contrast markedly with the tiny eyes of the insect-eaters. There are also fundamental differences in the brains between the two groups. These differences are so considerable that some authorities have suggested that the fruit-eating bats are not closely related to the insect-eating bats at all but instead are descended from some ancient creature connected to the colugos. Molecular evidence, however, suggests very strongly that all bats, big and small, share the same ancestry. But either way, it seems certain that the fruit bats did not appear until some time after the insect-eaters had established themselves in the air.

Some species of fruit bats are known as flying foxes. They are not quite as big as foxes but the name is nonetheless apt for their faces are indeed rather fox-like and most have a reddish-coloured fur. The largest have bodies that are

about a foot long and wings that measure five feet from tip to tip. Their thumbs still retain a claw, and their index fingers are free of the wing membrane and are used as a hook when clambering about through the branches.

Fruit bats roost out in the open in what, in Australia, are called 'camps'. These may be huge, with sometimes more than a million individuals. They are noisy, smelly places. The bats hang upside down from the trees, which have often lost most of their leaves as a result of the bats' activities. The animals are densely packed, wrapped in their skinny wings like giant black fruits. As the day gets hotter, they start fanning their half-opened wings to keep themselves cool and the whole tree seems to be quivering. They squabble with one another producing little spurts of activity as one is ousted from its perch, takes to the air and tries to find a vacant hanging space on a nearby branch. Urination, when hanging upside down, could soil the fur, so usually, before they do so, they will reach up and hook on to the branch with their second finger and hang head-up. Sometimes, however, one will remain in its normal upside-down position and deliberately allow its urine to trickle over its body. Perhaps it is a way of ridding itself of skin parasites. The next rainstorm will provide it with a good wash.

△ *Straw-coloured fruit bats roosting, Zambia*   *Bare-backed fruit bats, Papua New Guinea* ▷

Such vast numbers of animals visible, audible and smellable for miles, inevitably attract predators. Hawks and other raptors often perch in trees nearby, lazily contemplating their next meal. And if you look hard enough, you may spot a tree python, with its coils neatly draped over a branch in the middle of the colony, waiting perhaps to locate an immature bat that cannot yet escape by flight. But in spite of the presence of these predators, it seems that an individual bat is less likely to be attacked if it hangs among hundreds of companions than if it roosts in a tree by itself.

When evening comes, the bats set out to feed. The bigger species are so large and heavy that in order not to lose too much height on take-off, they beat their wings two or three times to lift their bodies from the vertical to the horizontal and only then unlatch their feet. Some fruit bats feed almost entirely on nectar and some species of tree rely on them to carry pollen from flower to flower as they feed. Such trees – among them certain mangroves, cacti, wild bananas and eucalypts – produce flowers that only open at night and are white or cream in colour and as a consequence are more easily seen by the bats in the darkness. Some of these blooms stand clear of twigs and leaves so that the bats flying in front of them do not entangle their wings. Others hang from long stems. The flowers not only produce nectar in quantity but also a very strong perfume so that the bats are able to detect them from long distances.

Most flying foxes, however, are only incidentally nectar-drinkers. The bulk of their food is fruit. They may travel twenty miles or more to find trees where it is just beginning to ripen. Many fruits are so full of water and contain so little sustenance that an individual bat can consume its own weight of them in a single evening, spitting out the indigestible pulp, swallowing the juice and quickly ridding itself of unwanted liquid. But on the way back to the roost, they may also excrete the seeds. Fruit bats can devastate a fruit farmer's entire crop in a single evening. But they are, nevertheless, prime agents in maintaining the fertility of the rain forest.

There is yet a third branch of ancient tree dwellers that some think are connected to the ancestral colugos. These developed a different way of using their hands to ensure their safety in the trees. They did not use them as hooks, nor as wings, but as clamps. The slender loris of southern India and Sri Lanka is one of their descendants. It moves through the trees and bushes at night. It is less than a foot long. It has no visible tail. Its body is covered in a soft greyish fur with black patches surrounding its huge eyes and a white line that runs down its face

◁ *Epauletted fruit bat feeding on figs, West Africa*

between its eyes to its little pointed snout. The name loris comes from the Dutch word meaning clown, for indeed it does remind one of a circus character.

The loris's hands are remarkable. Its thumbs are greatly enlarged but the second finger, the index, is reduced to a small stub. This means that the span of its grasp is very wide, enabling it to get a firm grip on quite stout branches. Its feet are modified in a similar way though the second toe on each foot, while very small, carries a claw that the animal uses for cleaning its fur. The slender loris moves slowly and with great deliberation, seldom letting go with one limb unless its other three are firmly attached to something. And its grip is spectacular. If we grip something for more than a minute or so, our muscles tire and begin to ache. The loris, however, has a special mesh of blood vessels in its wrists and ankles that ensure that the muscles in its hands and feet are kept lavishly supplied with oxygen. As a result, the energy within the muscles is continually renewed and a loris can maintain a firm grip on a branch for twenty-four hours continuously. If you are by yourself, you will find it almost impossible to detach one from its branch if it is disinclined to leave. As fast as you remove one limb it will reattach itself with another.

The slender loris has a cousin, the slow loris, which is somewhat bigger and

△ *Slender loris, southern India*   *Slow loris, Indonesia* ▷

lives farther to the east, from Assam into South-east Asia and across Indonesia to the Philippines. Its legs are neither as slender nor so long as its smaller cousin. Both kinds, however, move through the branches slowly and cautiously. In fact, their method of hunting relies on this. Having spotted an insect, a loris leans slowly towards it, while holding on firmly with its hind legs. Then it lifts both hands and only at a last moment, makes a sudden lunge and grab. Both kinds of loris actively mark their territories with smell, by dragging their rear ends over branches and also by depositing a few drops of urine on regular sites.

West Africa has a loris equivalent. It, like them, moves with great deliberation, which is why in some English-speaking parts of Africa it is known rather engagingly as a 'softly-softly.' It is more properly called the potto. Its hands and feet are modified in much the same way as those of the loris. The thumbs and big toes are very big indeed and point away from the others. Although it usually moves in a rather stately way, it can turn very swiftly and bite those who interfere with it. It also has another and very unusual weapon. Three of the vertebrae at the back of its neck have crests which pierce the skin and have horny points to them. If threatened, the potto will bury its head in its hands and hunch its shoulders. It weaves slowly from side to side and then suddenly administers a violent neck-butt, which is the more alarming because it is so unexpected.

The potto's neck spines appear to have another use as well as defence. Both male and female have large scent glands in the genital area. Those of the female are paired and so big that they have been called a pseudo-scrotum. A pair will roost together at night, hunched over one another, the neck spines of one in the groin of the other. The spines, it seems, stimulate the scent glands. Sometimes it is the female that is anointed in this way, sometimes the male. This reciprocal marking is a unique way of securing a pair bond and an indication of how important scent is in the potto's life.

Both the lorises and the potto are undeniably monkey-like. Their grasping fingers and toes have, except for the grooming second digits, not claws, but flat nails. Their eyes are large and point forward, and they have quite a high forehead. Yet they also have pointed snouts with moist nostrils, like dogs or civets. It is as though they are half-way to becoming monkeys. For this reason they are collectively known as prosimians – forerunners of the monkeys.

Galagos, often called bush-babies, also belong to this group. They live in Africa both west and east. Some are as small as mice and others as big as a domestic cat. Unlike the loris and the potto they still have a long tail. This is of considerable use to them, for the bush babies, while they have grasping hands and feet,

Bosman's potto, West Africa ▷

are nonetheless superb jumpers. Their tails serve as rudders as they sail through the air from branch to branch.

Smell is also very important in the lives of galagos. When they emerge from their nesting holes in the evenings, the first thing they do is to urinate on their hands. Having done so they rub their hands on the soles of their feet. They may repeat this performance several times before setting out to forage and then they do so about every hour throughout the evening as they move through the trees. Some suggest that this gives their feet an additional adhesion as they leap from one twig to another. It is certainly gets sticky as it dries. Although they have habitual paths through the forest, regularly taking off from the same branch and landing in exactly the same place, it is hardly likely that their scent marks are for route-finding. Instead, they probably serve as signals proclaiming to others of their own kind that this territory is occupied.

Galagos in captivity, if given a new branch or any new object in their enclosure, immediately mark it with urine so that after quite a short time, their territory becomes noticeably their own, even to human nostrils. If you regularly clean their surroundings with disinfectant to conform to human notions of cleanliness and health, the bushbabies will never settle and feel at home. It is only when the enclosure is detectably theirs from several yards away that they are likely to breed.

There are several species of galago in Africa. The smallest, the dwarf galago, is an engaging imp no bigger than a mouse. The biggest, the fat-tailed, is the size of a

△ *A Senegal galago leaping*   *Thick-tailed galago, southern Africa* ▷

heavily-built cat. Otherwise, they are very similar in appearance, with large orange eyes, greyish or brownish fur and cream under-parts. Since they are nocturnal, bright colours and vivid patterns indicating species are of no value to them. Instead that information seems to be conveyed in their calls. They communicate with high-pitched squeaks and twitters. Researchers, analysing these, found that they were much more varied than had hitherto been suspected and

it now seems that there are many more species of galagos than had been realised and that there are still more waiting to be identified.

At the time that prosimians were just evolving, the immense island of Madagascar split away from the eastern flank of Africa. Later, monkeys appeared in Africa and displaced many of the African prosimians, which may be why those that survive there today are all nocturnal. But the monkeys were unable to reach Madagascar. There one group of prosimians, the lemurs, were able to flourish. And there, in the absence of serious competition, they evolved to occupy many of the ecological niches that monkeys and other mammals occupied in Africa.

The smallest, the mouse lemurs, are very similar in size and general appearance to the African dwarf galagos. The biggest of them, the indri, is bigger than most African monkeys. It is the only one in the family that has lost its tail. It seldom comes down from the trees and does not swing from its arms like an ape, nor run along the branches like a monkey. Instead, it jumps, like its cousins the tiny galagos. Like them it has legs that are very long, a third longer than their arms. When it leaps, with a compulsive push from these powerfully muscled hind legs, it travels through the air with its torso vertical and lands, very often on

△ *Mouse lemur, Madagascar*

Indris, eastern Madagascar ▷

a trunk rather than a branch, still in that position. It can cover ten yards in a single bound. And as soon as it lands, without any adjustment of its limbs or a new summoning of strength, it can take off again so that when you watch them in the forest, they seem to bounce from trunk to trunk.

Indris are handsome animals. They appear to be wearing white furry tunics and leggings with black gloves and shoes, a black cape over the shoulders and a black face mask through which they stare with startling yellow-green eyes. They are exclusively vegetarian and feed throughout the day. Each small family group occupies its own patch of forest. When alarmed they hoot ferociously and morning and evening, they proclaim their ownership of their territory with a long wailing chorus, to which both female and male contribute. They may sing for several minutes at a time and can be heard over a mile away.

Each family also makes plain the extent of its territory by marking the branches with urine and secretions from their muzzles. When the female comes into season, the male will mark over thirty times every day. The female however, as is the case with most Madagascan lemurs, dominates the male. In addition to her partner, there may be several youngsters in the group. It is she and her daughters who feed first in the higher branches of the trees while all the males wait submissively below. Occasionally a male will lose patience and attempt to climb up and join the female as she breakfasts on the tender shoots but he is likely to get cuffed for such impudence.

The indri has a group of cousins, all of them with tails but otherwise very similar shaped bodies. If anything they are even more strikingly coloured. Most are white except for their head-gear. One has a brown cap, another a golden one, a third has a head that is entirely black from the neck upwards and yet another is pure white from tip to toe. Down in the semi-deserts of the southern parts of the island, they inhabit a strange thorny scrub dominated by Didieriea, a cactus-like plant unique to the island. It has columnar stems forty feet tall, tasselled at the top with brownish flowers and studded along their entire length with alternate rows of small circular leaves and ferocious spines. The sifakas leap between these vegetable pillars, sailing through the air from one, with their torsos vertical and grabbing the next with their hands and feet simultaneously.

Sometimes the sifakas are compelled to come to the ground in order to get from one patch to another. The difference in size between their short arms and long legs make it almost impossible for them to run on all-fours, so they stand upright. But they don't walk. Moving each leg alternately does not come easily to them. Instead they travel in the same way as they do in the trees. They bound.

Verreaux's sifaka, south-western Madagascar ▷

To keep their balance, they lift their arms to shoulder height, or even above their heads. A family of snowy-white sifakas proceeding from one patch of bush to another reminds one irresistibly of dancers moving with that combination of elegance and strictly disciplined footwork that you might see in classical ballet.

Sifaka families do not defend their territories with sound like the indri. Instead they rely entirely on scent-marking. The diademed sifaka, a particularly handsome species with a black crown, golden arms and legs, and black hands and feet, does so with particular assiduity. Females, having finished feeding will scent mark a branch and then leave. Immediately one of the males will rush over, sniff the site and sometimes bite at the scent mark, removing part of the tree's bark in the process. He then rubs his chest gland over the exact spot. Finally, he climbs up and smears scent on it from his anal gland. The reason for this is probably that sifakas, unlike indris, are promiscuous. Females will mate with whichever male takes their fancy. When they come into season, they broadcast their availability with their scent marks which have a strong and persistent perfume. If unattached males catch wind of it, they will sneak in and mate with the female if they can. Over-marking by the resident male seems to be his way of concealing his female's invitations.

One lemur spends most of its time on the ground. This is the ring-tail. It is the best known of all the family, for instead of being a strict vegetarian like its larger relations, it eats a wide variety of other things and consequently flourishes in zoos. It has a spectacular tail ringed with black and white and almost twice as long as its body and normally carries it vertically above its back, swaying gracefully as the animal runs about. All the prosimians, with their moist noses, are sensitive to scent and use it socially, but ring-tails do so in a unique and spectacular way. They fight with it.

They live in family groups of a dozen or so with a social system that is found nowhere else among mammals. As is usual among the lemurs, females are superior to males, but in ring-tail society each sex has its own hierarchy and all the females, even the most junior, are superior to all males, even the most senior of them. No other mammal has a comparable arrangement. Both sexes mark the group's territory though in different ways. The females, standing on their front legs, lift their rears to smear a tree trunk with secretions from their anal gland. The males do so with glands on their wrists. These have a horny pad growing alongside them. When a male marks, he reaches up to a sapling, grips it with his hands and with a sideways sway, scratches the bark with his wrist pad, making

◁ *Coquerel's sifaka, northern Madagascar*

an audible clicking noise. The action roughens the bark so that it collects the scent.

During the mating season, ring-tails raise their olfactory offensive to a higher more aggressive level. When a male start to spoil for a fight, he brings his tail forward over his back and draws it between his wrist pads so that it is anointed with scent. With weapons thus primed, the males then advance as a group towards the enemy. When battle begins, they throw their tails over their heads and thrash them from side to side. Waves of powerful perfume assault the nostrils of the enemy, who either find it so noxious or are so impressed by its strength that ultimately they retreat. It has to be said that this can only be deduced by human observers rather than experienced, for ring-tail perfume does not register in human nostrils.

It is not only the absence of other mammals that has allowed the lemurs to extend their ecological range. Woodpeckers, as well as monkeys, failed to cross the Mozambique Channel. The favourite food of these birds are larvae of wood-boring beetles. They find them by drilling into branches and tree trunks

◁ *Female ring-tailed lemur, with a baby on her back, scent-marking*

Aye-aye, Madagascar △

to reach the tunnels where the fat succulent grubs lie, gnawing their way through wood. To dine on such a diet requires first a detection device to discover where the grub lies and then equipment to cut through the wood to reach it. The aye-aye, by far the most specialised and indeed bizarre of all the lemur family, has evolved both.

The aye-aye is much the same size as the ring-tail with shaggy grizzled fur and a bushy tail. Its hands, however are quite extraordinary. The flat nails that make a prosimian's hand so human-like, have become long claws. The middle finger on each is like no other finger or toe. It has been elongated to grotesque lengths and lost most of its clothing of flesh so that it resembles a jointed rod with a hook on the end. This is the aye-aye's larvae-catching equipment.

The animal is a solitary nocturnal forager. Having found a likely branch, it puts its head down close to it and listens intently as it taps the wood with its middle finger. Perhaps the noise disturbs the larva and makes it move and the aye-aye can hear the faint rustle when it does so. Maybe, like a human doctor percussing a patient, it can detect both from the sound of the tap and the vibrations it causes where the wood is solid and where hollow. Having located an occupied tunnel the aye-aye then turns to carpentry. Its front teeth are particularly long and chisel-like and have open roots so that, like those of a rodent, the teeth grow just as fast as they are worn down. No other prosimian has such teeth. Indeed, they are so unusual and so like those of a squirrel that when the aye-aye was first examined by European scientists, they classified it as a rodent.

The aye-aye does not take long, with such equipment, to cut away the wood and expose the larva's gallery. Then the long bony middle finger becomes a bodkin. The aye-aye inserts it into the tunnel, probing and twisting it until its spike engages in the soft body of the larva so that it can pull out its squirming meal.

There is one prosimian that stands apart from all the rest in this group. This is the tarsier, which lives on the other side of the Indian Ocean, in Malaysia, Borneo Sulawesi and the Philippines. At first sight it looks very much like a small galago. It is the same sort of size as the dwarf galago, with the same soft fur and a long tail. It, too, has large eyes, grasping hands with flat nails on its fingers, and similar mobile crinkling ears which indicate excellent hearing. But it differs from all other prosimians in a number of ways.

First, in its diet. All others in the group eat fruit and vegetables, to some degree at least. The tarsier eats nothing but other animals. Insects such as beetles and cicadas, moths and grasshoppers form a major part of its meals, but it also

◁ *Aye-aye extracting larva from its hole*

will tackle with great relish and visible ferocity small lizards, nestling birds and even snakes.

Secondly, smell plays only a subsidiary part in its life. Whereas galagos impregnate their homes with it, pottos use it to bond with their mates, and ring-tails fight with it, the tarsier makes no greater use of it than to mark its territory.

Thirdly, its sight is much more acute than that of others. Its eyes are extraordinarily big. In fact they are the biggest in proportion to the size of the body of any mammal, each weighing slightly more than the tarsier's entire brain. If our eyes were as large in proportion to our skulls as those of a tarsier, they would be the size of grapefruits. Furthermore the tarsier's eyes are particularly sensitive. Uniquely among prosimians, the retina at the back of the eye has a groove down the middle which gives extra definition to its sight. Its neck is so mobile that it can be twisted through 180 degrees in either direction. When the animal's ears pick up the sound of an insect moving behind it, its head swivels round immediately and its sight is so good and its reactions so swift that it can pluck a fast-flying insect from the air with the skill of a cricketer making a difficult catch in the slips.

There is one further difference. It might seem so trivial as to be scarcely worth mentioning. The tarsier's nostrils, which project sideways, are circular. Fur grows almost to the edge of them and surrounds them, separating them from the upper lip. The nostrils of other prosimians, in contrast, are shaped like commas, permanently moist and linked to the upper lip by a strip of naked skin. This difference in the structure of the nose is a reflection of the smaller extent to which the tarsier relies on its sense of smell compared with other prosimians.

The only other clambering tree-dwellers that have noses like the tarsier are the monkeys. Those scientists concerned with working out the ancient lineages of the animal kingdom regard this as being of great significance. The tarsier, they believe, is the only prosimian that truly deserves that title. It, unlike the others, really is a 'pre-monkey', an ancient twig on the great branch that was to lead to that group. It was also, of course, the branch that led to ourselves.

◁ *Tarsier, Philippines*

9

THE SOCIAL
CLIMBERS

Monkeys are the most colourful of all the mammals. The ultramarine bottom of the mandrill is breath-taking. The mauve eyelids of the toque macaque are matchless. The golden lion tamarin has a coat of pure red-gold, a male vervet has a powder blue scrotum and the uakari a naked face that is as scarlet as a boiled lobster. The fact that these colours are often flaunted in sexual displays is a clear indication that monkeys also have the colour vision needed to appreciate such chromatic splendour. In fact monkeys, apes and ourselves are the only mammals that can perceive colour across the whole width of the spectrum. How and why did this talent develop?

It is plain that colour vision is of considerable value to those monkeys that eat fruit. It enables them to distinguish between those that are ripe and ready to eat and those that are still sour and likely to cause indigestion. That this should be possible is important for not only the monkeys but the plants. A fruit's sweet succulent flesh is an inducement to persuade animals to eat it and in the process swallow the seeds it contains. Then, after some hours and (with luck, as far as the plant is concerned) some distance away, the seeds will emerge in the monkey's droppings and land in a new location far from the parent plant. That strategy will fail if the fruit is eaten before the seeds are fully developed. So the fruit remains sour and, often, green until that has happened. Then it changes colour, signalling its readiness for consumption to potential seed-couriers. Cherries, strawberries and apples blush red, blackberries become a glossy jet black, and apricots turn orange.

This system did not evolve to suit monkeys in particular. It was in operation long before they appeared on the planet. The first flowering plants developed

◁ *Golden lion tamarin, south-east Brazil*

about a hundred million years ago. Birds and insects were both well established by that time, so it seems fairly certain that they must have been the plants' first customers. Tens of millions of years later, an early branch of the mammal family – the ancestral monkeys – appeared in the trees. They were probably looking for insects, the standard diet of most of these very early mammals. But sugary fruit tempted them too as it tempted birds and the need to select ripe ones and avoid indigestion may therefore have been one of the influences that caused monkeys to develop their colour vision in the first place.

Once they possessed that talent, monkeys were able to exploit it in other ways. They began to use it socially. Today, many still do so with spectacular effect. The red-faced uakari, for instance, has such a strange and dramatic appearance that catching sight of one suddenly and at close quarters in the forests of the Amazon can be almost alarming. Its colour is certainly one way by which members of the species recognise each other, but its particular shade also has a significance in an individual's social life. These monkeys live in groups of up to thirty. Each includes several adult males. The brilliance of their red faces and scalps varies from one to another. Research is now suggesting that the redder the male, the more resistant he is to malaria. The brightest have never contracted the disease at all. Females, it has been discovered, prefer to mate with the males who have the brightest faces. By doing that, they ensure, no doubt unwittingly, that their offspring have a better chance of being malaria resistant than if they mated with the paler ones. But these extraordinary monkeys are still little known and it may well be that their dramatic faces have additional functions in uakari society that we have not yet identified.

Life in the trees also demanded another visual refinement for the ancestral monkeys. They needed to be able to judge distance and so decide whether a branch was within reach of a stretch or a jump – or beyond either. So monkeys, early in their history, developed a pair of forward-pointing eyes that provide stereoscopic vision.

This advance in visual acuity – stereoscopy and colour sensitivity – is reflected in the shape and size of the monkey brain. The internal contours of fossil skulls give a good idea of the shape of the brain they once contained. So we know that the earliest monkeys had brains that were proportionately larger than their primitive cousins, the lemurs and bushbabies. As time passed and new species appeared, their brains not only increased in size but changed their proportions. The section processing signals from the eyes began to enlarge, whereas that part dealing with smell diminished. By about 25 million years ago their brain was much

Red-faced uakari, Brazil ▷

the same size and shape as that of the capuchin monkeys which today live in South America. They confirm the deductions about their ancestors' diminished sense of smell. It is rudimentary compared with that of other mammals such as lemurs or dogs. In fact it is hardly any better than ours.

Capuchins will eat most things – flower buds, leaf shoots, birds' eggs, small reptiles, even other mammals such as baby squirrels. Being omnivorous and prepared to eat anything is a sign of having a tolerant digestive system but not necessarily of great intelligence. However, capuchins do have an additional ability that suggests a lively and inquisitive mind. They are able to discover food in places that other animals might well ignore. And once an individual makes such a discovery, others in the community have the capacity to quickly learn about it. So different capuchin troops develop their own particular table manners, their own particular feeding culture.

In Costa Rica, among the mangrove swamps along the Atlantic coast,

◁ *Tufted capuchin monkey, South America*   *Brown capuchin monkey, Brazil* △

capuchins have discovered that clams, with the two halves of their shells tightly clamped together and apparently totally uneatable, in fact contain particularly tasty food. When the tide is out, the monkeys clamber down the mangrove trees and over the tangled arching roots to pick out the clams from the black mud. The shells are firmly closed and the capuchins do not have the strength in their jaws to crack them. But the monkeys have discovered another way of getting at the flesh within. They start hammering the shell on a branch. The clam continues to keep the muscle that holds its two halves together tightly flexed. The troop moves on but they take the clams with them, knocking them persistently on whatever is at hand. Eventually the clam's strength gives out. It has to relax the muscle and when it does, the capuchin gets a finger or a tooth between the two halves of the shell, tears them apart and scoops out the still writhing flesh. Young capuchins often sit beside the adults, ready to pick up any eatable fragments that the adult may drop. But they pick up more than that. They also watch and thus learn that if they have patience and work long enough at these unpromising objects, they too will get a delicious meal.

South American monkeys are more varied than those of Africa or Asia. The bearded saki monkey, in contrast to the capuchin, has a very restricted diet. It eats almost nothing but seeds and fruit. It is one of the most extraordinary-looking of monkeys with a huge shaggy tail, a bushy beard that extends half way down its throat and a bulbous swelling on top of its head.

Fruit flesh is not, in itself, very sustaining. A plant puts into it only the minimum quantity of nutriment needed to persuade couriers to eat it. The flesh of many fruits, therefore, consists of little more than fibres saturated in sweetened water. The real goodness is packed away inside the seed, ready to sustain the seedling when it germinates. Until that time, this precious store is well protected.

Sometimes, if the seed is comparatively small − a blackberry pip or a melon seed − its covering need not be particularly robust since the seed is seldom chewed and is likely to be swallowed unnoticed with the fruit's flesh. The only protection it needs is a coat that will resist a monkey's digestive juices on its passage through the stomach and down the gut. If however, the seed is larger, then its armour needs to be much tougher − as is the case with many tropical seeds such as those within the fruit of a mango or an avocado. Most monkeys will simply gnaw away the outer flesh and discard the central stone. But not the bearded saki, particularly when fruit is scarce. Its front teeth in both its upper and its lower jaw project forward, with the top pair hooking over the bottom so that

they are able to deal with such a stone almost as effectively as a parrot can crack a seed with its beak.

There are no winters in the great tropical forests of South America and trees may flower at any time throughout the year. Consequently saki monkeys can nearly always find fruit somewhere and since the flesh of fruit provides them with carbohydrates and the seed within with protein, they get all the sustenance they need. Nonetheless, they may have to travel considerable distances, for fruiting trees are often widely separated.

White-faced sakis are constantly on the move and are particularly well adapted to travel through the canopy. Their hind legs are considerably longer than their front legs. This enables them to jump from tree to tree, covering such distances that local people call them *monos voladores*, flying monkeys. This disparity in the length of their front and hind limbs, however means that walking on all fours is slightly awkward for them so, up in the tree tops, they will often run along horizontal branches standing upright with their arms above their heads.

△ *White-faced saki, Guyana*

Spider monkeys also have fore and hind limbs of unequal length, but in their case, it is the arms that are longer. They are not primarily leapers but brachiators. When travelling at speed, they move beneath the branches, using their hands as hooks that latch on to a branch and, with equal ease and speed, detach from it. To help in this, their fingers are extremely long and their thumbs are either greatly reduced and widely separated from the rest of their fingers or lost altogether. The tail is muscled, like those of other tree-climbers such as tamandua, binturong and kinkajou and can truly be regarded as a fifth hand for on the underside near the end, the skin is naked and equipped with minute ridges, abundant nerve endings and sweat glands, just as hands are. This extra prehensile limb is even longer than their arms and is so mobile that when the monkeys are feeding, they appear to be five-legged, almost justifying, to those who are not numerically pedantic, their name of spider monkey.

The South American howler monkeys dine on leaves, the most abundant food in the canopy. They have not evolved such complex techniques for digesting them as ground-living leaf-eaters, such as cud-chewing or faeces swallowing, but they do have that blind cul-de-sac, the caecum, and an enlarged lower intestine as elephants and horses do, that are full of microbial cultures which break down cellulose. Even so, they need to be selective in which leaves they pick. Once again, colour vision enables them to be so.

When many rain-forest leaves first burst from their buds, they are protected by bitter-tasting poisonous chemicals. As they grow, they become more fibrous and less digestible. Between these two conditions, there is a brief stage when they are both palatable and digestible. At that moment, they have a reddish-yellow colour, caused by the appearance of one of the substances that will be involved in photosynthesis. Young leaves at this stage in their development provide the best meals. The monkeys, with their colour vision, can easily identify them and then with their dexterous fingers, pick them out from the older, less edible ones. Even so, digesting leaves of any age takes a long time so howler monkeys spend at least half their daylight hours dozing after their meals.

But even though howlers eat great quantities of leaves every day, their food is so poor nutritionally that they do not have a lot of energy to spare. So the spectacular gymnastics of the white-faced sakis, the *monos voladores*, are not for them. But in fact, leaf-eaters do not need to move very far. Just as tropical trees do not all flower simultaneously so they do not all shed their leaves in one brief season as trees in temperate regions do in autumn. Instead they shed and replace their leaves continuously the year round. So there are nearly always

◁ *Woolly spider monkey with young, Brazil*

tender newly-opened leaves somewhere or other on a tree nearby and the howlers do not need to travel far to find them.

Even so, both males and females resent the approach of another group that might upset their domestic relationships and they warn others to keep away. They do not do so, however, in the way prosimians might do by marking the branches throughout their territory with smell. Instead they howl. The male has a special organ in his throat that enables him to produce one of the loudest sounds made by any land-living animal. It can be heard almost a mile away in the forest. The whole family join him, morning and evening, in an unearthly wailing chorus that echoes through the forest, giving notice that a family is in residence and has claims to the leaves in that part of the canopy.

One South American monkey, the douroucouli, has found a way of avoiding competition with other species. It has become nocturnal and goes looking for food at a time when all other monkeys are fast asleep. Its eyes are huge, so that its alternative English name of owl monkey certainly seems appropriate. These give them excellent vision in low light. Colour vision, however, is of little value at night, so the douroucouli's big eyes have lost their cones, those elements in the retina that detect colour. Instead they contain only rods, which

◁ *Male howler monkey calling, Costa Rica*   *Douroucouli, Panama* △

distinguish shape. Their eyes do not, however, have a tapetum, that reflecting membrane behind the retina of their eyes that so sharpens the low-light vision of bushbabies, cats and other nocturnal animals. Its lack suggests that douroucoulis only took to the night life comparatively recently. In their dark world, they have had to revive the sense of smell that other monkeys have reduced so substantially. They mark their routes through the branches by smearing them with perfume, using a small tuft of hair, just beneath the tail, that is impregnated with an oily secretion.

There is one part of the canopy that most monkeys find difficult to reach – the area just beneath the topmost layer of leaves where the twigs are so thin that they cannot support an animal of any real weight. The marmosets, however, have become so small that they can venture on to twigs without any danger. Their tiny hands cannot grasp anything thicker than a twig, so instead of gripping a branch in the way that their larger relatives do, marmosets run along them four-footedly and to help them keep a firm hold, their nails, except for those on their big toes, have become claws.

The pygmy marmoset is the smallest of all monkeys. It weighs a mere two and a half ounces – seventy grams, scarcely twice the weight a house mouse. A single cicada or spider is scarcely worth the attention of a normal-sized monkey, but for a pygmy marmoset such a morsel constitutes a reasonable meal and it snatches them up when it can find them. Its staple diet, however, is something that is completely ignored by most other monkeys.

Pygmy marmosets live in family groups half a dozen strong, each with its own patch of forest which the group vigorously defends. Within this territory stand one or two strange trees. Their trunks are marked by neatly spaced circular pits, each surrounded by a raised calloused ring. Anyone but an expert botanist familiar with the flora of the upper Amazon, where the pygmy marmosets live, might reasonably suppose that this is a tree he has never encountered before and that these rings are, perhaps, the scars left by leaf bases. In fact, they are the work of the marmosets. They are sap pits. The marmosets gnaw holes in the tree's bark, causing sap to flow. The tree responds by growing scar tissue, but the marmosets constantly renew and enlarge the wounds until a ring forms around each of them. The marmoset family visits each such tree in its territory every day to feed on the sap that accumulates in the pits and gnaw away at the pit rims to make sure that the tree continues to supply their needs.

These little monkeys are so small and defenceless that they could easily be taken by predatory birds or jungle cats, particularly when they are out on the

Pygmy marmoset, Amazon ▷

open tree trunk working at their wells, which is where they are for three quarters of the daylight hours. Not surprisingly, therefore, they are well camouflaged with inconspicuous brown coats.

However, other marmosets and their close cousins, the tamarins, that lead less conspicuous lives among the leaves of the canopy, have been able to develop all kinds of facial decorations that over the generations have had a particular appeal to the females and now serve as badges enabling them to recognise their own kind, in much the same way as the differently coloured plumage of closely related species of birds do. Marmoset ears have become insignia. In some species they are tasselled, in others bare. Some have black tufts, others white. Head crests serve the same purpose. One tamarin has a scalp with straight upstanding hair as white as cotton, another a hugely elongated moustache that droops around its chin and has given its owner the name of emperor tamarin. The golden-mantled saddle-backed tamarin has a black head, with a white chevron between its eyes, a grey back, orange arms and a red patch on its rump, whereas the golden lion tamarin has fur that is completely red-gold with a wonderful metallic sheen.

△ *Black-tufted-ear marmoset*
    Emperor tamarin ▷

Following pages, clockwise from top left ▷▷
black-chested moustached tamarin; common and
buffy-headed marmosets; cottontop tamarin

The forest is not rich enough in the kinds of foods these miniature monkeys need to sustain a dense population so marmosets do not form large troops as capuchins often do but live in family groups. Physically they are small enough to live in holes in tree trunks. A family may have as many as thirty such holes, widely distributed throughout their territories that they may use at various times. Typically, a marmoset family consists of a breeding female and one or two adult males together with a couple of their grown-up offspring. They are a tightly knit and apparently very affectionate group. When one member meets another after some time apart, they greet each other by arching their backs, brandishing their whiskers and combing one another's hair, conversing as they do so with high-pitched twitterings. Both the adult males mate with the female who nearly always gives birth to twins. They are non-identical but genetic finger-printing shows that they have the same father.

Rearing twins is a considerable labour, for the babies are not abandoned in the nest hole but carried about clinging to their parents' fur. The female has to eat a great deal in order to produce the milk her twins require. Transporting them would be a very considerable additional burden for her, so she usually hands them over to other members of the family who take the twins with apparent enthusiasm. There may even be minor disputes as to whose turn it is to look after them. The youngsters are groomed by their carers and when they get hungry are handed back to the female so that they can suckle.

When, after a few weeks, the twins are weaned, the young females in the group – the twins' elder sisters – collect food not only for them but for their parents. These young females may be over two years old, but their sexuality is repressed as long as they remain with their family. Only when one leaves and finds a vacant territory for herself will she be able to breed but by this time, as a result of helping to rear her younger brothers and sisters, she has learnt the necessary skills needed to be a good mother. Marmosets and tamarins are the only monkeys or apes to use this kind of cooperative breeding system.

The monkeys of the Old World – in Africa and Asia – differ from those of the New, the Americas, in several basic though seemingly trivial ways. The one that taxonomists used when naming the groups concerns their noses. Those of South American monkeys are flat and broad with widely-spaced nostrils that point to the side of the face, whereas African monkeys have rather thinner straighter noses and narrow nostrils that point forwards. The South Americans therefore are called scientifically platyrrhines – flat-noses, and the Old World monkeys are called catarrhines – hooked noses. There are also other anatomical characters that

Guereza colobus, East Africa ▷

define each group. Old World monkeys have two premolar teeth, New World, three. Old World monkeys have ear-drums which, like our own, lie deep in the skull at the bottom of a tube. New World monkeys have eardrums so close to the outer surface of the head that they can easily be seen within the ear. And there is one less technical and immediately apparent way of sometimes telling where a particular monkey comes from. If it has a prehensile tail, then it is a South American. For some inexplicable reason no adult African monkey possesses a muscled tail with which to grip a branch.

The Old World has its leaf-eating specialists just as the New World has. In Africa, these are the colobus. They digest their meals in large stomachs with separate compartments where colonies of cellulose-breaking microbes flourish. Like the spider monkey, they have either lost their thumbs or greatly reduced them. There are about a dozen different species. True to the monkey tendency, they are splendidly coloured. One group is basically black with white patches. The most spectacular of these is the guereza colobus that lives in forests from the Congo to Kenya. It is a magnificent animal with black fur on its body but a long mantle of white hair flowing down its flanks and a pure white tail. Another group of colobus contains species that are basically a gingery red. They don't have such long capes but they vary considerably in the coloration of their faces with caps and cheeks that may be different combinations of grey, black or red.

The variations in the basic coloration of colobus species has more to do with geography than with communication. The black and white species that lives at considerable altitude in the mountains of Ethiopia and Kenya has a longer mantle and thicker fur than those that live in the lowlands of the Congo. That is to be expected. They need thicker coats to keep themselves warm at altitude. Red colobus have been affected by geography in a different way. When Africa started to dry about 30,000 years ago, the great forest that covered much of the centre of the continent Africa was fragmented by the spread of the grassy savannahs. The communities of red colobus living in pockets of forest that today are only tenuously connected or even cut off from one another began in–breeding. As a consequence they slowly changed physically, just as many species confined on islands eventually become slightly different from the parent species on the mainland.

Asia too has its leaf-eaters – the langurs of India and the leaf monkeys of China and South-east Asia. The golden snub-nosed monkey, one of the leaf-eaters, lives in southern China and as far west as Tibet and south as Burma and northern Vietnam. It has a bright orange cape over its shoulders, a white muzzle and a blue turned-up nose. This glamorous creature when it was first discovered by

European scientists in the nineteenth century, was named by a French taxono-mist, *Rhinopithecus roxellana*, meaning Roxellana's nose-monkey. Roxellana was a celebrated sixteenth century Russian courtesan who was said to have red hair and a nose which was delightfully retroussé (though not, one imagines, blue). Another snub-nose lives in Yunnan. That one, instead of having orange shoulders is predominantly black. A third living only on one mountain in Guizhou province, is grey.

Borneo has a leaf-eater, the spectacular proboscis monkey. The female's nose is turned up and not unlike Roxellana's. The male however has achieved unparalleled nasal dimensions. His nose is so big it droops down below his chin. When he grunts, it jerks upwards. Since it is only the males that develop this extraordinary feature it must presumably have some significance in court-ship.

The Old World's generalised all-purpose, omnivorous monkeys, equivalent perhaps to the New World capuchins, are the guenons. Most of them are pri-marily forest livers and as many as six different species may occupy the same

Golden snub-nosed monkey, China △

area. Each, however, finds its food in a different part. One feeds in the topmost branches, another close to the ground. Yet another keeps close to the banks of any waterway running through the forest. Under these circumstances, it becomes of particular importance that an individual monkey should know whether another it glimpses in the dense vegetation of the forest belongs to a different species. The guenons do this by facial signals, as marmosets do. The spot-nose guenon has, as its name suggests, a bright white spot on its nose, the moustached a white chevron on its upper lip. The red-eared has not only red ears but yellow cheeks, the red-tailed has blue skin around its eyes and white cheeks as well as its red tail. The de Brazza's monkey, one of the most handsome of them all, has a black face with a pure white muzzle, an orange tiara, a white beard, a white stripe down each thigh and a blue scrotum.

Guenons, like all monkeys, live in groups. Some, like those of the vervet, may contain as many as fifty individuals. This is of great value in defence. Many pairs of eyes, between them, are more likely to detect approaching danger than

269

◁ *Male proboscis monkey, Borneo*   *De Brazza's monkey* △

just one. In such circumstances, swift communication between individuals is essential. Colour signals, no matter how vivid, may not be immediately noticed by all. Sounds do the job much more efficiently. But danger can come in many forms and from many directions. If a snake appears, sliding across the ground towards a group of foraging vervets, a warning call will send individuals to scamper up into the trees for safety. But that would be exactly the wrong thing to do if in fact the danger comes from an eagle circling in the sky above. So monkeys have several different alarm calls. Vervets use at least five, which indicate not only the direction from which the threat comes, but also whether the danger is relatively trivial or one that demands urgent defensive action.

Individuals in the troop can recognise one another's voices. They even know those belonging to members of neighbouring troops, and react very strongly if a human investigator plays a recording of an individual in an unexpected place. Mothers know not just the sound of their own babies but recognise those of others. Youngsters call for help. Males vocally threaten rivals. A dominant male will bark an order telling juvenile males to stop squabbling and use another to warn of the approach of a rival group. All in all, investigators working with vervet monkeys have identified a vocabulary of at least 36 different calls.

Impressive though this is, it cannot be accurately called a language. Languages have syntax and grammar. 'The cat sat on the mat' does not mean the same as 'the mat sat on the cat'. No one has yet demonstrated that any monkey changes the meaning of its calls by changing the order in which it makes them. Nonetheless, monkeys can use their calls in very subtle ways. They can even tell lies. One observer documented an occasion in which an individual sat watching another laboriously excavating a large tuber. Just as it was about to pull its prize from the ground, the watcher shouted the snake alarm. The digger shot up into the trees and the watcher ran over and picked up the tuber.

Gestures can also be extremely eloquent. Aggression is signalled by staring and raising the eyebrows; submission by presenting the hindquarters as if offering to copulate; friendliness by smacking the lips, as though eating and by individuals grooming one another.

Such gestures may be modified in order to exploit to the full an individual's particular coloration. So when a de Brazza's guenon signals his aggression, he shakes his head, drawing attention to his white bearded dewlap. The mona monkey, on the other hand, bobs up and down and flaunts his white chest. A senior male vervet, strolling through his companions as they forage out on the

271

Vervet monkey, East Africa

open savannah may notice a young male, junior to him who is sitting in a desirable position, perhaps near a female or in a patch of shade. If he wishes to assert his seniority, he will move over towards him. Junior may submissively get to his feet and allow himself to be displaced. If he is reluctant, the dominant male may send a more emphatic signal. He stares and raises his eyebrows to expose his pale eyelids. If that doesn't have the effect he wants, then he will parade backwards and forwards in front of junior, and even stand up on his hind legs to give junior a full view of his vivid blue scrotum and his penis which is a startling scarlet against the white of his underbelly. If that does not have the proper effect, then there is likely to be a physical fight.

In North Africa, on the other side of the Sahara, live relations of the guenons, the macaques. Those in the coniferous forests of the Atlas Mountains in Morocco are an isolated branch of a family that is today primarily Asiatic, and found right across Asia from Afghanistan, across India to Thailand, China and Indonesia, and from Sri Lanka in the south to Tibet in the north. There are fifteen species or more. The one in Japan is one of the few primates, apart from mankind, to live outside the tropics and has become famous for bathing in hot springs during the bitter Japanese winter. Another is the rhesus monkey, once used so widely in medical research, which lives as far north as Afghanistan.

△ *Japanese macaques bathing in hot springs*   *Lion-tailed macaque, south-eastern India* ▷

Yet another lives in Europe – on the Rock of Gibraltar. Once, when the climate was warmer, this species occupied many parts of Europe including Britain, as we know from fossils. With the onset of the Ice Age, some 300,000 years ago, they retreated southwards until they were restricted entirely to southern Spain. Whether today's Gibraltarians are the last descendants of those ancient Europeans is uncertain. Reliable records of them only go back as far as the eighteenth century. Some say they are descended from pets brought back from Africa and released in Roman times. But importations of them from North Africa have been frequent, the most celebrated in recent times being that made under the instructions of Winston Churchill who wished to ensure that the legendary prediction that the British would leave Gibraltar if the monkeys did would not come true.

Most macaques spend so much of their time on the ground that their tail is no longer of much use to them. It is not prehensile, like that of South American monkeys, and they hardly need its help in balancing on the ground. To some extent it is used in signalling, but in cold weather, it can be a real liability, for such long thin extremities lose a lot of heat and are susceptible to frost bite. So the tails of macaques have either been much reduced or completely lost. The Indonesian species, which clambers around mangrove swamps feeding on crabs, still has a

△ *Barbary macaque, Gibraltar*

respectably sized tail. Another, that has a wide distribution from India to Vietnam has a reduced tail and is known, perfectly accurately as the stump-tailed macaque. The Moroccan species however has lost its tail completely and that has led to it being given a highly inaccurate name. It is sometimes called the Barbary 'ape'.

Baboons spend even more of their time on the ground than macaques. They have lost many of the characteristics that make other monkeys such capable climbers. Their hind legs are not elongated for jumping but are about the same size as their front legs, so they can move easily and efficiently across the ground in a four-footed way. A female, like all female monkeys and apes, becomes sexually fertile on a regular cycle. It is important that males should know when this is, so a female signals her condition every month in an unmistakable and very obvious way. As she approaches the peak of her fertility, so her bottom swells and turns bright red. The males keep a close eye on this, and when the moment is right, seek to copulate with her.

Should an adult female fail to conceive, her bottom, when she next becomes sexually receptive, will swell to an even greater size. In the wild, the attentions of the males are such that this seldom happens. In zoos, however, it may well

Sexually receptive female baboon △

be that a female cannot find a mate. Then, as she fails to conceive, cycle after cycle, the swelling on her rear becomes grotesquely big, a sad sign of the deprived conditions in which she is being kept.

When a baboon's infant is born, five months or so later, it too is colour-coded. The adults are a sandy brown or an olive green, according to the species. All baby baboons, however, are black with bright pink faces, a uniform that tells other members of the troop that an infant is among them who needs special care and attention lest it should stray or get into trouble. Several other species of Old World monkeys draw attention to their young in this way. The baby

produced by a black and white colobus is pure white, that of a silvery South-east Asian langur, bright orange, and that of the stump-tailed macaque, a primrose yellow.

Most species of baboon will eat virtually anything – insects, lizards, roots, fruit. Some are efficient and ruthless hunters, killing young antelope fawns if they get the chance. One species, the gelada, once thought to be a true baboon but now placed in a genus all of its own, has become a total vegetarian. It lives high in the Simien mountains of Ethiopia where there is nothing much for a baboon to eat except grass. But they do not have sharp incisor teeth, like sheep or rabbits. Instead they have to use their dexterous hands to pluck the grass, tuft by tuft. They sit on their haunches in the sunshine, sometimes in troops several hundred strong, slowly working their way across the grassy mountain slopes. That, however, gives them a communication problem. How can they continue to use the standard baboon communication system of showing one another their bottoms every time they need to amiably greet one another or send

◁ *Langur monkey with her orange baby, South-east Asia*

Troop of geladas grazing, Ethiopia △

messages about their sexual availability? To have to get to their feet every time would cause serious disruption in their feeding – and like all leaf-eaters, they have to spend a major part of their day doing so. The geladas have solved this problem by, in effect, wearing their bottoms on their chests. Right in the middle, above their breast-bone, they have a patch of scarlet naked skin. It is this that has given them their alternative name of bleeding heart baboon. So when a senior male walks through a feeding group, requiring the submissive signals due to his rank, his juniors remain sitting and feeding and merely swivel round to show him their chests.

The female gelada uses the same system to send sexual invitations. Those, of course, vary according to her sexual cycle. Her rear is, like those of all her baboon relatives, naked and pink, and like that of others, it expands and intensifies or diminishes and fades according to her sexual condition. But she also has a duplicate signal on her chest. As she approaches oestrus, so both her bare patches, fore and aft, expand to almost alarming proportions. Small pink bead-like spheres around the margins on her chest also swell, mirroring similar changes to the pattern on her rear.

Geladas cannot establish particular friendships and alliances, as in most other monkey communities, by continually grooming one another. Their hands are only too busy collecting grass. So social grooming is conducted vocally. They have a vast repertoire of rhythmic and melodic vocalisations. They exchange calls varying from gliding swooping yelps to quiet grunts, and all the time their hands are busy, plucking yet more leaves of grass. Their near-continuous vocalisations are the monkey equivalent of the daily gossipy conversations over the fence in a human community.

The basic unit in gelada society is a band of females. They usually have a favoured male who lives alongside them and mates with them when each comes into season. To maintain this favoured position, he has to compete and sometimes fight with challenging males. With a premium on size and strength, the males have become very big indeed, half as heavy again as the females and with dramatic capes of long hair on their shoulders. Their size is doubtless attributable to the advantage it gives in winning battles between themselves, but the long capes are more likely to be the result of the females' choice. In a social system where just one male mates with all the females in the group, his physical characteristics quickly become entrenched. If females have a preference for a mate with particularly long hair and maintain it over many generations, then males will tend to acquire longer and longer hair, often with remarkable speed.

Male gelada, Ethiopia ▷

But even the spectacular displays of the gelada pale in comparison with those of the baboon-like monkeys that live, not out in the open on savannahs, but in the gloom of the deep forests of West Africa.

The drill is a huge baboon. The male's head is surrounded with a white fringe. His face is black and naked of hair. Its skin has the polished firmness of a carved wooden mask, through which his small orange eyes glare with startling effect. His hairy coat is a sandy brown. His buttocks are monstrous. They are swollen and project beyond the end of his spine. They shade from white into lilac and become purple at the outer margins.

Yet even he is outdone by his close cousin, the mandrill, which lives in the same forests. The male is the biggest of all monkeys. He weighs nearly 80 pounds (36 kilos) and stands 20 inches (50 centimetres) high at the shoulder. He has similar spectacular buttocks, but his face is even more grotesque. A scarlet streak runs from between his eyes down to the tip of his nose. There it broadens to cover his nostrils and his upper lip. On either side of his nose, he has ridges of naked skin that are electric blue. The grooves between them are purple. This extraordinary face is surrounded by a band of white fur with above a brown crest and below an orange beard.

△ *Adult male drill, West Africa*

A male mandrill ▷

Such astounding, extravagant faces go far beyond what is required to identify an animal's species. Nor can it be attributable to mild variations in a basic pattern occurring in an isolated population. It can only be the result of female preference. Mandrills, like geladas, are polygamous. Each dominant male lords it over a harem of around thirty or more individuals, of whom twenty or so are likely to be adult females. There may also be one or two other males in the same group. But they are juniors, slimmer and not nearly so brightly coloured. It is the dominant male's brilliant colours which, at one and the same time, attract females to join him and repel junior males, so preventing them diluting the genes that are responsible for his magnificent colours. For generation after generation, females mated with the most brightly coloured male they could find. So over centuries of such selection, the mandrill's face, the most brilliantly coloured image displayed by any mammal, has become more and more spectacular. An ancestral taste for fruit, and a need to identify ripeness, has led over the millennia to the monkey's equivalent of the peacock's tail.

10

FOOD FOR
THOUGHT

Some thirty million years ago a monkey-like creature was living on the grass-lands of Africa that then were spreading across many parts of the continent. It was about the size of a baboon and its forelimbs were almost the same length as its hind, suggesting that it was as at home on the ground as it was up in the trees. It was already identifiably different from its cousins in South America, both in its teeth and the structure of its ears. Its descendants in Africa were destined to divide, in another ten million years time, into specialist leaf-eaters, like the colobus, and those with a more generalised diet such as the guenons and the baboons. But before these species appeared, another branch of its descendants spread eastwards into the forests of tropical Asia.

There they took permanently to the trees and developed their own special way of moving among the branches. They lost their tails and their arms became greatly elongated so that they could swing rather than clamber. Today they do so with such skill and astonishing speed, that they are the most breath-takingly acrobatic of all tree-dwelling mammals. They are the gibbons.

Gibbons are sometimes called 'lesser apes'. There are up to fourteen different species of them living in the forests of South-east Asia from eastern India through the Malaysian peninsula to Sumatra to Borneo. They are the only primates, apart from human beings, who form permanent monogamous families, a male and a female with one, two or more rarely three of their young living closely together. These families seem to be closely-knit. In some species, members seldom move more than twenty five yards away from one another. Gibbons will nibble leaves and occasionally catch insects which give them valuable protein, but their main food is fruit. Although that is available all the year

round in their forests, they need a large area to provide them with the quantity they require, so each gibbon family lays claim to its own extensive patch of forest.

Each species has its own characteristic coloration but they are all various combinations of brown or black usually with a white frame around the face. They have none of the bright colours or visual patterns common among monkeys, for visual signals are not a very effective way of communicating between different groups of animals that are as widely dispersed as gibbons. They use a different method of sending their messages of territorial defence or sexual invitation to families in nearby territories. Like howler monkeys, they sing.

The gibbons' song echoing across the mist-blanketed forest at dawn can be heard from five miles away. It is the sound that is likely to wake you if you spend any time travelling through these forests and its haunting music will remain in your memory for ever thereafter. The song is usually repeated many times in morning sessions that may last for up to a quarter of an hour. Different species have their own particular variant of this pattern and their own characteristic voices. The male siamang gibbon which lives in Malaya and Sumatra has a pouch on his throat that balloons out as he sings and acts as a resonator,

285

◁ *Female lar gibbon and young, Indonesia* *Male siamang gibbon singing, Sumatra* △

amplifying his calls. The female in most species takes the major role with the male providing a coda at the end. In some species the pair duet, each with its own part. In others the two may sing in unison. The most accomplished singer of all is said to be the little pure black species, Kloss's gibbon, that lives on the Mentawi islands off the west coast of Sumatra. Male and female sing by themselves. The female's 'great call' lasts for up to forty-five seconds. It starts with a long series of pure, slowly ascending notes. Then she introduces trills that build into a bubbling crescendo. As her song rises to a climax, she leaps into the air and hurtles from branch to branch, tearing off sprays of leaves and throwing them to the ground. It's a truly barn-storming performance.

Feeding and travelling in the very top storey of the forest, of course, limits an animal's size. You can't leap about at such speed from one tree to another in the way that gibbons do if you are big and heavy. For one thing, the branches would break. But there is an alternative way of getting around, particularly if you are content to remain a little further down in the trees. Orangutans, which live alongside gibbons in Sumatra and Borneo, weigh up to 200 pounds (90 kilos). Like gibbons, they are primarily fruit eaters but large animals have large appetites and there is seldom enough in one area to feed a whole family. As a consequence,

△ *Adult male orangutan, Sumatra*   *Young orangutan sheltering from rain, Borneo* ▷

orangs live largely solitary lives and do not have permanent territories. Instead individuals range widely through the forest. This has an effect on the relative size of the two sexes. When a female becomes sexually receptive, several males in the neighbourhood may become aware of the fact. Drawn together by her, they may quarrel. Vicious fights may develop before the issue is settled. So the biggest male in the neighbourhood is likely to father the great majority of the next generation and over many generations, male orangs have become very much larger than the females. They can be terrifyingly big. In Borneo, the males develop fleshy flanges on their cheeks, framing their faces. Sumatran males have long beards and moustaches. Both develop enormously long shaggy coats of red hair and grow so huge and heavy that they find it easier to travel any distance on the ground rather than through the branches.

Orangs are clearly very intelligent creatures and have considerable manual dexterity. Each evening they build nests for themselves in the tree tops, bending over branches to form a springy platform. If rain threatens, they may even construct a roof. To drink, they will insert a long hairy finger into a tree-hole

filled with water and then raise it so that the water trickles down into their pursed lips. They are equally dexterous in extracting honey from the nests of bees that build their combs in tree holes. To collect ants or termites, they break off twigs, sometimes chewing the end to form a kind of brush. They then use these tools to chip away at a nest. Young orangs who stay with their mothers for three or four years doubtless learn these techniques from her.

Orangutan investigating water, Borneo △

Even so, their behavioural range seems small compared with that of other great apes. It may be their solitariness, rather than a lack of intelligence, that limits it. Evidence to support this comes from the swampy forests on the northern tip of Sumatra. Here flood-waters regularly inundate the forest and as a result many of the trees produce fruit in great quantities. So here there are twice as many orangs in a square mile of forest as anywhere else. The orangs feast in particular, on the seeds of the Neesia tree. But the Neesia tree does not rely on animals to distribute its seeds. That job is done by the waters that regularly flood into the forest. The seeds, accordingly, are not wrapped in sweet flesh to tempt animals to swallow them but protected from those that might make a meal of them by a hard husk covered in stinging hairs. And that works well.

In most parts of Sumatra, orangs ignore Neesia fruit. But not in these northern forests. Here the orangs have discovered how to open them. The technique is quite complicated. First the stinging hairs that cover the husk have to be removed. To do that, an orang produces a special tool, a twig cleaned of its bark. Holding this in its teeth, it carefully cleans off the unpleasant hairs. Then it opens the fruit by ramming a piece of wood into a crack and forcing the husk apart until it is possible to hook out the seeds with a finger. Doubtless it was one particularly innovative individual that devised the technique many years ago. But because here, thanks to the abundant food supply, adults sometimes feed together, the skill has spread by imitation and these northern orangs have a culture that differs from that of any other group. So the comparative simplicity of orangutan behaviour elsewhere may be connected to the fact that scarcity of food prevents them from living in groups.

Africa also has a giant ape, the gorilla. It is even bigger than the formidable male orang. An adult silverback male can weigh over 400 pounds, twice as much as an orang. He is by far the biggest and heaviest of all living primates. With a crest of hair on the top of his head, and an immensely broad chest he can be truly terrifying, particularly since he makes it his responsibility to protect his family and will charge any intruder who seems to threaten them. Domestically, however, in his own family group he is a peaceable vegetarian.

The sub-species that lives in the dense forests of the western Congo eats a significant amount of fruit and often climbs to collect it, provided the trees are strong enough to carry its weight. In the mountains of the east however, there are not nearly so many fruit-bearing plants and the eastern sub-species, the mountain gorilla, has to exist almost entirely on leaves – giant celery, nettles and vines. Because of the low nutritional value of such a diet, much of the

mountain gorilla's day is spent feeding. They make themselves beds at night, bending over branches to form a springy mattress but otherwise, they show no particular inclination to be inventive and indeed have no need to devise novel techniques to find food.

Africa's commonest ape, the chimpanzee is very different. It is an omnivore. Whereas a mountain gorilla lives largely on just half a dozen different plant species and may never sample more than fifty in its whole life, a chimp eats over three hundred species and will take the leaves or fruit of over twenty in a single day.

They collect insects such as ants and termites. They catch small lizards and rob birds' nests of their eggs or young. They are also meat-eaters and regularly hunt, catching and killing monkeys, young baboons and duikers. Such a wide diet allows them to live in large groups. Some troops consist of only a dozen or so, but there are others over a hundred strong. Within such communities, discoveries once made are quickly shared. So chimps have learned to fish for termites by poking sticks down the holes in a termite hill. They extract water from tree holes in the wrinkles and folds of a leaf, specially crumpled and

◁ *Lowland gorilla with young, Congo*   *Chimpanzee cracking nuts, Tanzania* △

creased for the purpose. They crack nuts by collecting them and taking them to special places in the forest where there happens to be a conveniently-shaped stone that can be used as an anvil. Then they place a nut in the best position and strike it smartly with a piece of wood or a smaller stone.

The size of their communities also enables them to collaborate and so obtain food that a single animal could not get for itself. They hunt in teams. In the tall dense forests of the Ivory Coast, chimps regularly catch monkeys. A single chimp could hardly expect to do so by itself for it weighs twice as much as most monkeys. Consequently, monkeys can escape along branches that would break under the weight of a chimp. So chimp hunters, to be successful, are compelled to work together.

They have a well-practised technique. Having located a troop of red colobus, their usual prey, feeding in the tree-tops, the hunting party starts to track it. When the monkeys move into a patch of forest that suits the hunters, one of the male chimps, often an older more experienced one, will quietly and unostentatiously run ahead and take up a position in the top of one of the trees. Then other males, rather more obviously, rush up on either side of the colobus troop, climbing swiftly hand over hand. The monkeys take fright. With the rest of the chimp troop advancing towards them on the ground and threatened on each side by young males in the trees, there is only one way to go. They run and jump through the branches, straight towards the old male concealed in ambush ahead of them. As they get within his reach, he suddenly springs out, seizes one and quickly kills it with a swift bite on its back. The chimps following along the ground are now screaming in excitement. The ambusher does not sit up in the trees feeding on his catch. He brings the little body down to the ground and there hunters and onlookers gather round to take a share. It is unlikely that everyone will get a mouthful. The body of a colobus is not large. But it is nonetheless divided between females as well as males, spectators as well as hunters. Indeed, it is sometimes the case that the male who made the kill does not even get any meat at all.

Chimpanzees are the closest of our animal relatives. It is often said that we share 98% of their genetic material. That figure can easily be misunderstood. The elements in DNA should not be thought of as ingredients in a recipe for a cake. Genes are rather like instructions to a computer, any one of which can radically change the nature of its displays. Even so, the connection between chimpanzees and humans is certainly very close indeed. They must share a common ancestor.

◁ *A chimpanzee using a tool to feed on termites*

It is more difficult to be precise about when the descendants of that ancestor split into two branches. It was probably around five million years ago. Some time after it happened, the humanoid branch made an important development. They began to walk upright.

The most dramatic evidence of this having taken place was discovered in Tanzania in 1978. A team of palaeontologists had discovered a bed of rock composed of ash that been discharged from the nearby volcano of Sadiman. Measurements of the radioactivity of its particles make it possible to date that event quite precisely. It happened three million six hundred thousand years ago. The ash was rich in carbonates and a shower of rain that fell soon afterwards turned it into a kind of plaster. Several animals walked across it while it was still moist and the tracks set hard. The palaeontologists could still see the twin slots of antelope hooves, the footprints of a primitive horse and large circular depressions with their rims curled up and outwards by their maker's weight that may been left by a kind of rhino. And among these, to their astonishment, they saw a long continuous trail of human footprints. There are clearly two sets, one significantly bigger than the other. Perhaps the big one was made by a male and the other by a female. The two trails are so close that their makers could well have been in physical contact. Perhaps they were walking hand in hand. The bigger ones are more scuffed and blurred than the smaller set and expert trackers have deduced that this was because a third slightly smaller individual was walking behind the big one, treading in its tracks. Maybe the newly wet ash was slightly caustic and unpleasant to walk through and a youngster was following behind the male treading in his footsteps. At one point, you can see that the female (if that indeed was the smaller one) has halted in mid-stride. Perhaps she glanced back at something. It is a tiny moment in the life of a small family, caught and preserved for three and a half million years.

Two hugely important deductions can be made from these vivid prints. First, there is no wide gap between the big toe and the rest, which means that the makers, whoever they were, no longer habitually climbed trees like apes. They were ground livers. Second, there is no sign whatever of any knuckle prints. These creatures, without any question, were walking upright.

There are few more contentious issues in the story of humanity's evolution than the explanation of what it was that caused four-footed knuckle-walking to be abandoned in favour of a two-footed stride. There are several theories. Maybe it was to allow our ancestors to carry things in their hands – food that they had just collected, a simple stone tool that had taken some time and skill to chip into

The Laetoli footprints, Tanzania ▷

effective shape, or maybe an infant that lacked the clasping hands and feet needed to cling to its mother like a baby ape. Maybe it was to get a clearer view over grass-covered plains to spot a stalking carnivore. Maybe, if the climate was as hot as some believe, it was to minimise the amount of the body exposed directly to the sun out on the open plains– just the shoulders and the top of the head, instead of the whole length of the torso.

There is yet another theory that was first proposed half a century ago and is often dismissed by many as far-fetched. Nonetheless it still has its adherents. Some six million years ago, this part of Africa was rent apart by earth movements associated with the formation of the Rift Valley. Sea water poured in from the Red Sea away to the north. Isolated patches of higher ground turned into islands and great areas became shallow lagoons. If that happened, then there would un-doubtedly be a great deal of food to be collected on the margins and in the shal-lows of such lagoons – shellfish, crustaceans, small fish. Intelligent inquisitive primates would surely have been quick to exploit such a new and rich food sup-ply. Doubtless those early humanoids would have soon discovered a way to crack open molluscs and tear apart crustaceans just as capuchins and crab-eating ma-caques do today. Maybe some went into deeper water to look for food or to reach new feeding grounds on the shores of nearby islets. If they did, an upright stance would have brought them great advantages, not the least of which was that it enabled a female to carry her baby above the water.

A vivid picture of such a scene in reality comes from some islands in the delta of the Congo. There chimps that have been individually rescued from lives of deprived captivity have been released in order that they may learn to fend for themselves in the wild before they are given total liberty. While they are doing so, they are provided with daily supplies of bananas. As the boats of those caring for them approach every morning, the chimps wade out towards them two-footedly, anxious for their bananas. The males sometimes hold their long arms above their heads, with hands clasped. Females come too holding their in-fants high on their chests. With the water supporting their body and helping their balance, an upright stance comes easily to them and with their shorter bowed ape-legs hidden by the water they look extraordinarily human, except for their jutting jaws and low receding foreheads with heavy eyebrow-ridges. In fact they look uncannily, eerily, like the many reconstructions that have been made over the years of creatures that might have been the link between apes and hu-manity. As these chimpanzees have become more accustomed to their new, if temporary homes, they have become more confident in the water. It is usually

said that chimps do not swim. Perhaps that is the case in normal circumstances, but one at least of these males has shown that if there is a need to do so, they certainly can. He has now started to swim out, way beyond his depth to get to the food-carrying boat first.

Could living near and occasionally in water have been the circumstance which led mankind's ancestors to move from knuckle-walking to full bipedalism? Proponents of the theory invoke several pieces of anatomical evidence to suggest that humanity did indeed have an amphibious phase. Human beings, compared to chimps and orangs, have next to no body hair. Why did they lose it? In water, hair is a relatively ineffective insulator. In consequence, many water-living mammals – seals, whales, hippos – have lost theirs. Hair runs in tracts that form runnels down which water trickles away. The tracts on the body of a four-footed animal run down at right angles to its spine, across its flanks to its belly. Our hair tracts, such as they are, however, are different. Instead of running roughly parallel to our ribs, they run at right angles to them, down from our shoulders parallel to our spine, suggesting that we were already

Chimpanzee wading to reach food, Congo △

standing upright when our bodies were just as hairy as that of a chimpanzee. Our skin differs from that of all other living apes in another way. It has abundant sweat glands that produce an oily secretion. That too is an adaptation that could be very valuable for a creature that lived in and out of water. Particularly persuasive is the fact that when we develop fat, we accumulate it in a layer immediately beneath our skin. The only other mammals that develop subcutaneous layers of fat in this way are seals and whales – and they do so to insulate themselves from the chilling water. If our ancestors had spent a significant amount of time in the water, such a fat layer would have been very valuable.

If that crucial shift in posture did indeed happen when our remote ancestors were living in and around lagoons, it would also help to explain how another important change occurred at this time – a huge increase in the size of our ancestors' brains. Developing and operating a brain takes a lot of energy. Fruits, seeds, roots and other vegetation are sufficient to fuel ape-sized brains. We, however, have gigantic brains, by far the largest in proportion to the size of our bodies of any species of mammal. Keeping them functioning consumes 20% of all the energy that we get from our food, even though our brain accounts for only 2% of our body weight. Evolving a large brain could only have happened among creatures that had an abundant supply of rich food. Shellfish would have provided exactly that.

Whatever the cause for humanity's adopting an upright stance, there is no doubt that these vertical apes needed a rich diet. Meat of some kind would have been of the greatest value to them. How could they have obtained it, once they left the shores, if that is where they first stood upright, and ventured out on the grasslands? They were not sufficiently fast on their feet to run down an antelope. They did not have dagger fangs like a lion that could stab an animal to death or carnassials to slice meat from a carcass. Nor did they have powerfully muscled jaws with grinding teeth to enable them to crush bones like a hyena. Nonetheless, they used their manual dexterity to fashion weapons, and their high intelligence to work out ways to hunt. So they became meat-eaters.

Many tribal people can find, track and kill an animal with skills that beggar the belief of anyone who was not born and reared in a wilderness. A few of them who still retain the ancient nomadic way of life have an understanding of the animals they pursue that seems to verge on the supernatural. One such are those living in the Kalahari Desert, who were once known as Bushmen. Their language makes use of up to seven different click sounds which written European languages have no letters to convey. These are accordingly represented, albeit

Bushman hunting, Namibia ▷

crudely and indiscriminately by an exclamation mark or a slash. Thus, the name these people use for themselves is written as !Kung. The acuteness of their observations when tracking is beyond European comprehension. From what seems the faintest blur in the sand, they are able to deduce not merely what kind of animal made it, but very often its sex, its condition, and the time that has passed since it was there. And they will be able to distinguish it thereafter from other individuals of the same species.

When hunting, they often use small arrows tipped with poison. One such, hitting an animal near a blood vessel close to the surface of its skin will ultimately be lethal. But death may be a long time in coming and a !Kung hunter may have to follow its spoor for days before the animal collapses. An even more ancient and arduous method does not require any weapons whatsoever, only an endurance beyond our imagining. Having found possible prey, an eland perhaps or a giraffe, the hunter frightens it so that it runs. He then follows at a steady pace and catches up with it so that before it is properly rested, it is put to flight once more. The pursuit continues in this way, through the hottest part of the day and beyond. It may take hours. It may even take days. Eventually the animal, deprived of any food or drink, collapses. But the hunter has also suffered and may be close to collapse himself with barely enough strength to

complete the kill. It is a technique that the !Kung may have inherited and preserved from the far reaches of human history.

But catching and killing an animal is only half way to getting a meal. The meat of most wild animals is too tough to be masticated by human teeth. To make a meal of what he has caught, the !Kung hunter uses another skill that is unique to humanity. He makes fire. A dry pointed stick twisted rapidly between the palms of his hands with its point pressed on another piece of dry wood first produces a smoking black powder and then, blown carefully, flames. Once the fire is going properly, the carcass is thrown on it. Heat breaks down the fibres of the flesh, softening them so that they can be more easily chewed. Tough vegetable food such as seeds and tubers, treated in the same way, also becomes digestible. So the skill of fire-making brought a whole new range of foods within reach of humanity.

It seems that human beings continued living in this way – hunting animals and gathering fruits, seeds and roots – for tens of thousands of years. At first this new species was rare, but as its numbers slowly increased, it spread across Africa. Then, around a million years ago, these creatures moved out of the continent, rounded the eastern end of the Mediterranean and spread westwards into Europe and eastwards into Asia. Although these beings were recognisably human, and had a stance and bodily proportions much like ours, their faces were still considerably different. They had a low forehead, large eyebrow ridges and, perhaps most striking of all, massive protruding jaws. They were indeed upright men, *Homo erectus*, but they were not yet modern human beings, *Homo sapiens*.

Slowly they evolved a larger and larger brain. As their cranium expanded to accommodate it, so the proportions of their faces changed and by fifty thousand years ago, their skulls were almost identical to ours. Such people lived in the caves of France and Spain. By now they had a range of very efficient tools – wooden spears, harpoons with multiple teeth to hold fast a slippery fish and stone tools of varying sizes from small scrapers to the elegantly chipped roughly triangular weapons known as hand-axes. And thirty thousand years ago, in the far recesses of their caves, by the light of burning sticks and rushes, they drew pictures of the animals with which they shared the land.

We still are not sure – and perhaps never can be – exactly why they went to such trouble to draw these astonishingly beautiful designs. A very likely explanation, however, is that it was connected in some way with the hunts on which they depended. The animals they drew are those which we know, from the

remains of bones, were the ones which they used for food – horses, bison and cattle.

Some of the animals have lines scored in their flanks that could be interpreted as representing spears. Others have marks that look as though they might have been literally stabbed by a weapon. One famous design in the French cave of Lascaux shows a bison partially disembowelled. It is tempting to assume, therefore, that the paintings were part of some kind of ritual aimed at bringing success in the hunt and maintaining the continuing abundance of the animals which by now provided the people with a major part of their diet.

But still human beings had done nothing practical to change the abundance or distribution of the animals and of plants they fed upon. They had, however, recruited help for their hunts. Dogs were the first wild animals to become mankind's servants. The relationship may well have started as a mutually beneficial partnership. Man and wolf both sought the same prey. Wolves could track it with their sensitive noses much more effectively than man. Man, on the other hand, with his spears, could wound and cripple an animal without getting to

Palaeolithic painting of disembowelled bison, △
Lascaux, France

close quarters. So maybe both species hunted together and shared the spoils, the human families cooking their chosen parts of the carcasses, the dogs hanging around the encampments clearing up what was left and enjoying the warmth and protection of a fire at night. The relationship was made the easier since wolves were by nature social animals, accustomed to accept the leadership of a dominant individual. The human hunter thus acquired a pack of canine helpers.

Human beings were still wanderers, able to move wherever the hunting was best. If the herds migrated, the human hunters could follow them. Human beings still do. In Scandinavia, the Lapp people follow the reindeer herds. In West Africa, the Peul, the Bororo and other groups still follow the cattle as they move each season to where the grazing is best. Such people claim to own the animals they follow and to have tamed and domesticated them. But the herds still migrate as they have always done, and the people have to move likewise.

Elsewhere, where the pastures were richer, it was possible for people to confine the animals they ate. The first steps towards domestication must have taken place when hunters killed a female with young and brought the infants

◁ *Saami woman herding reindeer, Lapland*   *Bororo herder following long-horned cattle,* △
Cameroon

back to camp where the women reared them, perhaps giving them milk from their own breasts. Such animal orphans, growing up within the settlement, had little fear of people when they became adult. So eventually groups of human beings acquired herds of sheep and goats, cattle and horses, that lived and travelled with them.

Plants continued to be a part of the diet of the human omnivore. At the eastern end of the Mediterranean, ten thousand years ago, the people collected, among their vegetable foods, the seeds of a wild grass. Such seeds are not easy to gather. If you pick the grass before the seeds are ripe, they are so small and hard that they are barely worth eating. On the other hand, if you leave them until later they may well have fallen from the stem and you will have to pick them up one by one. In fact there may only be a couple of days in the year during which the harvesting of a particular kind of grass in any one area is practical. So when the time was right, it was sensible to gather all you could and take it back to your encampment to save for harder times.

One of these wild grasses, emmer, is likely to have been gathered more frequently than most, for it keeps its seeds attached to its stem for significantly longer than other grasses. When the people brought bundles of it back to their camps, some seeds were inevitably spilt and in due course, they germinated. From such a start it was only a small step to deliberately scatter the seeds in spring and recover the grain, increased many times, in the summer. This modest grass was the ancestor of wheat. In eastern Asia, at around the same time – about ten thousand years ago – other people were also discovering another kind of grass with similar characteristics – rice. To begin with, this grew in forest clearings but over the centuries ways of cultivating it in shallow flooded fields were developed.

So by taking control of their food supply and moulding animals and plants to meet their own needs, human beings were able to settle down on permanent sites close to one another. No longer was the size of their communities dictated by the natural productivity of the patch of territory on which they lived. With more and more food available and close at hand, the size of communities increased. The first towns began to develop. Now it became possible for some people to free themselves from the daily chore of producing food. Instead they were able to develop particular skills and technologies – forging metals, weaving cloth, firing pottery – and acquire food by exchanging it for their handiwork. So began the development of skills and the sharing of knowledge that within a few millennia were to lead to mankind's dominance of the whole world.

But sometimes those basic techniques for producing food fail. That seems to

Terraced rice, Guangxi province, China. ▷

have happened in central America. A thousand years ago, great cities stood there surrounded by forest. Their inhabitants, the Maya, had developed a complex and highly sophisticated culture. Their astronomers understood the solar cycle and were able to predict celestial events with great accuracy. Their mathematicians were the first in the world to develop the concept of zero. They kept accurate and detailed calendars and recorded their history in books and on spectacular standing stones, using a system of complex glyphs that we have only just managed to decipher. And they built temples that were the tallest buildings in the whole of the New World until the first skyscraper was constructed in Chicago in 1886.

Then around five hundred years ago, disaster struck. Within a century, the population virtually disappeared. The temples were abandoned and the surrounding forest encroached and covered them. What was the cause of this catastrophe? Was it a dreadful decimating disease? A peasant revolt against the scholars, the priests and the aristocrats who had accumulated such vast riches? Some insect pest that ravaged and destroyed the crops on which the people depended? There is no evidence for any of these things.

The answer has only become clear in the last few years. Ever since the forest-cloaked temples were first discovered by Europeans in the nineteenth century, it has been assumed that these spectacular buildings were ritual centres, inhabited solely by priests and aristocrats and visited only occasionally by the rest of the population. The common people, relatively few in number, were thought to have lived in small homesteads scattered through the forest where they practised shifting agriculture, clearing ground to grow their food and, when the soil was exhausted, moving on to another site. Now however, excavations are beginning to show that the stone temples were not the only buildings to stand on these sites. Once they were surrounded by closely packed wooden-walled thatched houses. Some of these cities are thought to have housed as many as 40,000 inhabitants. How could so many people, packed into such a small area feed themselves?

They did so by practising an intensive agriculture. They terraced the hillsides. In the lowlands they built dense networks of fields and canals. Now these areas are buried under lush tropical vegetation but their outlines are still visible in the right light from the air. Pollen grains, trapped in deposits of mud, provide a record of what plants grew in the area at any one time. They reveal that by the time the temples were built, most of the surrounding forest had been felled and replaced by a great expanse of cultivated fields. Excavations in the foundations of

dwellings and the fields beside which they stood show clear evidence of soil erosion. Some of the houses seem to have been completely buried by silt and debris washed from the fields.

The soil in a tropical rainforest, unlike that which forms in a temperate woodland, is very poor in nutrients. For a few years after clearing it will give reasonable yields of crops but it has to be allowed to lie fallow regularly and for some time. The Maya, as their population continued to increase, were forced to cultivate their fields more and more intensively and continually cut down more of their forest to make additional fields. Eventually, the time came when the fields could yield no more. Skeletons excavated from these sites and dating from the later periods show evidence of malnutrition. Starvation spread. The size of the population fell rapidly. The cities could no longer be maintained and were abandoned. The rain forest reclaimed the territory it had lost.

Elsewhere in the world, within the next few hundred years, other technologies enabled people to build even bigger cities. Chicago, at the beginning of the nineteenth century, was a small town on the shores of Lake Michigan. To-day the city covers over two hundred square miles and provides homes for over

The Maya city of Tikal, Guatemala △

three million people. Cattle by the million are brought in by trucks and by rail to be slaughtered to feed the city's teeming population. The plains around the city have been stripped of their rich and varied vegetation, sprayed with chemical poisons to eliminate insects that might damage the crops, and planted with a cultivated strain of wheat that has become so in-bred that it is now sterile.

When human beings built their first cities around the eastern end of the Mediterranean there were only about five million people on the whole planet. When the Mayan people built their temples in Central America there were ten times as many – fifty million. Two hundred years ago, as mankind's technological inventions spread round the world and created the industrial revolution, the human population had grown to two thousand million. Today, it stands at over six thousand million. The last thousand million were added in the last decade. All these millions need food.

As our numbers increase, so space for other animals and plants decreases. Our skills and technological ingenuity seem to know no bounds. Having ventured to every corner of our planet, we are now beginning to look beyond it. We are conducting experiments to find out how to grow food to sustain ourselves should we manage to extend the territory of our species to Mars.

Men impressed their footprints on the moon a mere three and a half million years after the first of them to walk upright left theirs across a field of volcanic ash in Africa. That is a mere blink in the eye of evolution. In that short time we, alone among all animals, have discovered how to exploit our environment to produce more and more food to sustain our unparalleled numbers. In so doing we have denied the earth to other species to such an extent that many have been driven into extinction and many more are now trembling on the brink.

Perhaps the time has come, when we should put our aspirations into reverse. Perhaps now, instead of controlling the environment for the benefit of our population, we should find ways of controlling our population to ensure the survival of our gravely threatened environment.

◁ *Chicago by night*

ACKNOWLEDGMENTS

It may seem that a television naturalist immediately knows the name and detailed behaviour of every animal he happens to encounter. It is not, of course, like that. Research teams have helped him select the animals which he goes to film, and field scientists who have studied the animal in question for years have primed him with information, some of which may well, as yet, be unpublished. And even after he has seen the animal in question and he seeks to write some account of what he has seen, his companions will help to sort out his observations and share his deductions. This is certainly so in my case, and were it not for such people I would not have been able to write this book.

While I was writing, I was also helping to film the programmes for the BBC series that has the same title. Any television series involves a considerable number of people and this one was no exception. The names of the team are listed below. All concerned helped in one way or another but I have two particular debts. First, to the producers with whom I debated each programme; and second, to Alex Griffiths and Dan Tapster who bore the brunt of library research that was necessary before the first outlines of the series could be devised and who subsequently undertook meticulous checking. I am also greatly indebted to Professor Colin Groves who generously read a draft of the manuscript and steered me away from error.

In the two and a half years that it took to make the television series, many researchers working in the field advised us on where and when to go to film the particular animals that we wished to show, engaged in particular activities that interested us most. They also told us most generously of the things they had observed. Without their help the cameramen working on the series could never have captured the sequences they did and I would have failed to understand or even see a great deal that I now treasure. Among them are: in Australia, Henk Godthelp, Tanya Rankin and Peggy Rismiller; in New Zealand, Brian Lloyd and Rod Morris; in India, Toby Sinclair; in the United States, Jim Brandenburg, Paul and Sue Schurke, and Peter Smallwood; in Canada, Brock

Fenton; in Africa, Natasha and David Breed, Louis Liebenberg, Olle Moita, Jessica Tombs and Klaus Zuberbuhler; in Borneo, Ashley Leiman; in South America, Judy and Louis Arroyo, Charles Foerster.

I am very grateful to them all.

Executive Producer
Mike Salisbury

Producers
Huw Cordey
Mark Linfield
Neil Lucas
Vanessa Berlowitz

Assistant Producers
Anuschka de Rohan
Chris Cole
Dan Eatherley
Jonathan Keeling
Kathryn Jeffs
Sean Christian
Sharmila Choudhury

Researchers
Alex Griffiths
Dan Tapster

Production Manager
Alison Brown-Humes

**Production
Co-Ordinator**
Alison Tancock
Lisa Connaire
Sue Storey

Production Secretary
Susan Endacott

Finance Assistant
Chiara Minchin

Field Assistants
James Aldred

Jeff Wilson
Tom Clarke

Music
Ben Salisbury
Dan Jones

Graphic Design
Mick Connaire

Colourist
Jonathon Prosser

Sound Recordists
Chris Watson
Graham Ross
Trevor Gosling

Film Editing
Andrew Netley
Dave Pearce
Jo Payne
Martin Elsbury
Pete Brownlee
Stuart Napier
Tim Coope

Dubbing Editors
Angela Groves
Kate Hopkins
Lucy Rutherford
Paul Fisher

Dubbing Mixers
Martyn Harries
Peter Davies
Stephen Williams

Photography
Andrew Anderson
Barrie Britton
Bill Wallauer
Brian McDairmant
Charlie Hamilton James
Dave Houghton
David Rasmussen
Doug Allan
Eric Huyton
Gavin Thurston
Jamie McPherson
Jeff Hogan
Jeff Turner
Jim Clare
Justin Maguire
Justine Evans
Mark Lamble
Mark Payne-Gill
Mark Smith
Martyn Colbeck
Michael Male
Mike deGruy
Mike Potts
Neil Bromhall
Owen Newman
Paul Atkins
Paul Johnson
Paul Stewart
Rebecca Hosking
Ron Shade
Rory McGuinness
Shane Moore
Simon King
Warren Samuels
Warwick Sloss

SOURCES OF PHOTOGRAPHS

Frontispiece (Getty Images) Anup Shah

10 (Nature Picture Library) Mike Potts

13 (BIOS) Hubert Klein

15 Erwin & Peggy Bauer

15 Günther Ziesler

17 (Auscape)
D. Parer & E. Parer-Cook

19 Günther Ziesler

21 (Oxford Scientific Films)
Bert & Babs Wells

23 (BIOS) Hubert Klein

24 (Oxford Scientific Films)
Hans & Judy Beste

25 *above* (Auscape)
D. Parer & E. Parer-Cook

25 *below* (Auscape) Mike Gillam

26 (Auscape) Ferrero-Labat

28 (Auscape) Jean-Paul Ferrero

30 (Animals Animals) Howie Garber

31 Günther Ziesler

33 (Auscape) John Shaw

34 (Animals Animals) Fred Whitehead

39 (Oxford Scientific Films)
Tim Shepherd

40 (BIOS) Laurent Thouzeau

42 (NHPA) Daniel Heuclin

43 (Okapia) Skip Moody

45 (Oxford Scientific Films)
Tony Tilford

47 (Nature Picture Library) Jim Clare

48 (Oxford Scientific Films)
Michael Fogden

50 (Hedgehog House) Brian Lloyd

51 Gerald Cubitt

52 (Natural Science Photos)
Pete Oxford

53 (Natural Science Photos)
Steve Downer

55 (Nature Picture Library)
Mark Payne-Gill

56 Günther Ziesler

57 (Bruce Coleman)
Alain Compost

59 (Hedgehog House)
Kevin Schafer

60 (NHPA) Jany Sauvanet

62 (FLPA) M. B. Withers

63 (Natural Science Photos)
M.W. Powles

64 (Animals Animals)
Nigel J.H. Smith

65 (Animals Animals) Marisa Pryor

66 (BIOS) Ruoso Cyril

68 (BIOS) Ruoso Cyril

70 (Nature Picture Library)
Vincent Munier

71 (Hedgehog House)
Shaun Barnett

72 (BIOS) Alain Mafart-Renodier

73 (Okapia) W. Wisniewski

74 (Oxford Scientific Films)
Wendy Shattil & Bob Rozinski

75 (Nature Picture Library)
Carl Englander

76 (Animals Animals)
Raymond A. Mendez

78 (Oxford Scientific Films)
Raymond A. Mendez

79 (Nature Picture Library)
Neil Bromhall

80 (NHPA) Anthony Bannister

82 (Oxford Scientific Films)
Marty Cordano

83 *above* (Nature Picture Library)
Paul Johnson

83 *below* (NHPA) Alan Williams

84 (Bruce Coleman)
Gordon Langsbury

87 (Bruce Coleman) M.P.L. Fogden

88 Rodney Griffiths

91 Günther Ziesler

93 *above* André Baertschi

93 *below* (FLPA) Gerard Lacz

94 Gerald Cubitt

95 Gerald Cubitt

96 Art Wolfe

97 Günther Ziesler

98 Erwin & Peggy Bauer

100 (Oxford Scientific Films) Alan Root

104 (Hedgehog House) Colin Monteath

108 Erwin & Peggy Bauer

110 (Auscape) Ferrero-Labat

111 (Nature Picture Library)
Peter Blackwell

112 (Okapia) John Cancalosi

114 (Nature Picture Library)
Derek Bromhall

115 Steve Bloom

116 (Nature Picture Library)
Peter Blackwell

118 (Natural Visions) J.M. Pearson

119 (Nature Picture Library)
Kennan Ward

120 B. & C. Alexander

123 (FLPA/Minden pictures) F. Lanting

125 (Nature Picture Library)
Brian Lightfoot

126 Alan & Sandy Carey

128 (FLPA) Gerard Lacz

129 B. & C. Alexander

130 (Hedgehog House)
D. Fernandez & M. Peck

132 (Bruce Coleman) Hans Reinhard

133 (NHPA) David Middleton

134 (Natural Science Photos) Ken Cole

135 (FLPA) E. & D. Hosking

136 (Oxford Scientific Films)
Stan Osolinski

137 *above* (BIOS) M. & C. Denis-Huot

137 *below* (Nature Picture Library)
Bruce Davidson

138 (Nature Picture Library)
Bruce Davidson

141 (FLPA) T. Whittaker

142 (NHPA) Nigel J. Dennis

143 (NHPA) Anthony Bannister

145 (NHPA) Andy Rouse

146 (NHPA) Andy Rouse

147 *above* (Natural Science Photos)
Pete Oxford

147 *below* (Bruce Coleman)
Günther Ziesler

148 (NHPA) Martin Harvey

149 (Auscape) Ferrero-Labat

150 (Oxford Scientific Films)
Belinda Wright

151 (Auscape) Ferrero-Labat

152 (Hedgehog House) Kevin Schafer

153 Erwin & Peggy Bauer

155 (Natural Science Photos) G. Kinns

157 (Bruce Coleman) Pacific Stock

158 (Nature Picture Library) Neil P. Lucas

160 (Hedgehog House) Kevin Schafer

162 Erwin & Peggy Bauer

163 Erwin & Peggy Bauer

164 (NHPA) Andy Rouse

166 (Nature Picture Library) Jim Clare

167 (Animals Animals) Michael Dick

168 (Bruce Coleman) Werner Layer

169 (FLPA) Wendy Dennis

170 André Baertschi

171 *above* (BIOS) Regis Cavignaux

171 *below* (Bruce Coleman) Alain Compost

172 Art Wolfe

173 (Bruce Coleman) P. Kaya

175 (Animals Animals) Paul Berquist

176 *above* Art Wolfe

176 *below* (NHPA) Stephen Dalton

177 (Animals Animals) Pat Crowe

179 Erwin & Peggy Bauer

180 (Bruce Coleman) Rod Williams

182 (BIOS) Gilles Martin

185 (Bruce Coleman) William S. Paton

187 (Bruce Coleman) Jeff Foott

188 (Nature Picture Library) Jeff Foott

190 (Oxford Scientific Films) Lon E. Lauber

192 (Natural Science Photos) B. Cranston

193 (Hedgehog House) Tui De Roy

195 (Oxford Scientific Films) Tui De Roy

196 (B. & C. Alexander) Paul Drummond

197 (BIOS) Christian Meyer

197 (Okapia) Fred Bruemmer

198 Erwin & Peggy Bauer

200 (Bruce Coleman) Rinie Van Meurs

202 (Biofotos) Heather Angel

203 (Nature Picture Library) Todd Pusser

205 (FLPA) F. Nicklin

206 (Okapia) Henry Ausloos

207 Neil P. Lucas

209 (Hedgehog House) Kerry Lorimer

210 (Nature Picture Library) Sue Flood

212 (Auscape) Francois Gohier

214 (Nature Picture Library) Anup Shah

215 Erwin & Peggy Bauer

216 (BIOS) Jany Sauvanet

217 (NHPA) Jany Sauvanet

218 (Oxford Scientific Films) Alan Root

219 (FLPA) Hannu Hautala

220 (Animals Animals) Mark Stouffer

221 (NHPA) Stephen Dalton

222 Gerald Cubitt

224 (Natural Science Photos) C. & T. Stuart

225 (Nature Picture Library) Michael Pitts

226 (Oxford Scientific Films) Partridge Films Ltd.

228 (Animals Animals) C. Dani & I. Jeske

229 (BIOS) Alain Compost

231 (NHPA) Daniel Heuclin

232 (NHPA) Stephen Dalton

233 (Oxford Scientific Films)
     Konrad Wothe

234 Gerald Cubitt

235 (NHPA) Nigel Dennis

237 (Natural Science Photos)
     Pete Oxford

238 (Animals Animals) Patti Murray

240 (Nature Picture Library)
     Pete Oxford

241 (Animals Animals)
     C. Dani & I. Jeske

242 (NHPA) Martin Harvey

244 (Nature Picture Library)
     Martin Gabriel

246 (Auscape) Rod Williams

249 (FLPA) Foto Natura Stock

250 (Auscape) Erwin & Peggy Bauer

251 (Roving Tortoise) Tui De Roy

253 Steve Bloom

254 (NHPA) Kevin Schafer

256 (FLPA) Jürgen & Christine Sohns

257 (Animals Animals) Marie Read

259 (Oxford Scientific Films)
     Partridge Films Ltd.

260 Erwin & Peggy Bauer

261 (NHPA) James Carmichael Jnr.

262 *above* (Oxford Scientific Films)
     Michael Dick

262 *below* (Natural Science Photos)
     David Lawson

263 *above* (Nature Picture Library)
     Rod Williams

263 *below* (BIOS) Seitre

265 (FLPA) David Hosking

267 (Nature Picture Library)
     Miles Barton

268 (Natural Science Photos)
     C. Dani & I. Jeske

269 (Natural Science Photos)
     C. Dani & I. Jeske

270 Frederick D. Attwood

272 Erwin & Peggy Bauer

273 (Auscape) Rod Williams

274 (NHPA) David Watts

275 (NHPA) Peter Pickford

276 Gerald Cubitt

277 (BIOS) Michel Gunther

279 (BIOS) Michel Gunther

280 (Animals Animals) Zig Leszczinski

281 (Hedgehog House) Kevin Schafer

284 (Animals Animals) John Chellman

285 (Animals Animals) Phyllis Greenberg

286 (Animals Animals) Zig Leszczinski

287 Erwin & Peggy Bauer

288 (Nature Picture Library) Anup Shah

290 (Oxford Scientific Films)
     Andrew Plumtre

291 (Oxford Scientific Films)
     Clive Bromhall

292 (Oxford Scientific Films)
     Stan Osolinski

295 Kenneth Garrett

297 (Nature Picture Library)
     Karl Amman

299 (Okapia) Safari/Okapia

301 (Semitour Périgord) Jean Grelet

302 B. & C. Alexander

303 (Hoaqui) E. Valentin

305 (Oxford Scientific Films) Keren Su

307 (FLPA) Derek Hall

308 (NHPA) G.I. Bernard

INDEX OF MAMMALS

The names of mammals used in the text are here accompanied by their scientific names.
Figures in **bold** type refer to pages with illustrations.